Intervention
Assessments

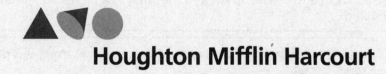

Houghton Mifflin Harcourt

Contents

Contents (continued)

Introduction

The *Intervention Assessments* provide screening, diagnostic, and progress-monitoring assessments to identify students who are at risk for reading difficulties and provide recommendations on the amount of support students are likely to need during reading instruction.

At the beginning of the school year, use the Screening Assessments to screen all students for reading difficulties. For Kindergarten and Grade 1, use the Letter-Naming Fluency and Phoneme Segmentation assessments to obtain an idea of a student's skills upon entry into the grade level and again at the middle of the year. Grade 1 also includes Screening Assessments of Nonsense-Word Reading and Word Identification, and a mid-year test of Oral Reading Fluency. In Grade 2, Screening Assessments include Word Identification and Oral Reading Fluency. In Grades 3–6, the Screening Assessments test grade-level Oral Reading Fluency.

Use the Diagnostic Assessments to follow up with students who demonstrated reading difficulties on the Screening Assessments and to inform targeted instruction. These tests include a Print Concepts Inventory, Letter-Sound Fluency, and a Phonological Awareness Inventory, and provide essential information about students' performance.

Use the Progress-Monitoring Assessments to monitor progress of students who are receiving intervention instruction and to help determine when they are ready to exit the intervention program. Each grade level has several tests designed to assess students' reading ability throughout the school year.

Screening for receptive and expressive vocabulary deficits is also recommended, although efficient measures in this area are limited. Your district reading specialist may recommend a screening instrument.

See the Recommendations for Data-Driven Instruction later in this book for guidance on using the results of the *Intervention Assessments* to help ensure all students receive the instruction they need to become successful readers.

Test Overview

Screening Assessments Overview

The Screening Assessments can assess quickly and efficiently several areas that are highly related to success in beginning reading. These beginning-of-year tests are given early in the school year to provide preliminary information on a student's performance on the essential skills and strategies necessary to be a successful reader with grade-level instruction. In Kindergarten and Grade 1, they are given again at mid-year to provide information about the student's progress. Your observations of students during phonemic awareness, letter naming, and/or letter-sound work will also provide information to help you plan instruction. Based on the results of the Screening Assessments and other observations, you will be able to determine whether students would benefit from intervention instruction or require additional diagnostic testing.

Letter-Naming Fluency

Kindergarten and Grade 1 The Letter-Naming Fluency tests are individually-administered tests that assess a student's facility at naming uppercase and lowercase letters. See page T10 for a more detailed description of the Letter-Naming Fluency tests.

Phoneme Segmentation

Kindergarten and Grade 1 Phoneme Segmentation is an individually-administered oral test designed to assess a student's ability to identify the individual sounds in a spoken word. See page T11 for a more detailed description of the Phoneme Segmentation test section.

Nonsense-Word Reading

Grade 1 Nonsense-Word Reading tests are individually-administered oral tests designed to assess a student's ability to sound out and read nonsense words using letter-sound associations (phonics). See page T12 for a more detailed description of the Nonsense-Word Reading tests.

Word Identification

Grades 1 and 2 Word Identification tests are individually-administered oral tests designed to assess a student's ability to read high-frequency and multisyllabic words. See page T13 for a more detailed description of the Word Identification tests.

Oral Reading Fluency

Grades 1–6 Oral Reading Fluency passages in Grades 1–6 are individually-administered, student-read oral tests to assess a student's oral reading skills. These tests focus on fluency, accuracy, and rate as well as provide important information about the student's decoding strategies by using specific grade-level targeted vocabulary. See page T14 for a more detailed description of the Oral Reading Fluency tests.

Diagnostic Assessments Overview

The Diagnostic Assessments provide information on a student's performance on the essential skills and strategies necessary to prepare and become a successful reader. Use these assessments based on students' performance on the Screening Assessments.

Print Concepts Inventory

The Print Concepts Inventory is an individually-administered interview designed for students who have not yet learned to read independently. It assesses a student's familiarity with print, directionality, and written language. See page T16 for a more detailed description of the Print Concepts test.

Letter-Sound Fluency

The Letter-Sound Fluency test is an individually-administered test that assesses a student's ability to associate letters with sounds. The teacher points to a letter, and the student makes the sound associated with the letter. See page T20 for a more detailed description of the Letter-Sound Fluency test.

Phonological Awareness Inventory

The Phonological Awareness Inventory consists of a series of individually-administered oral tests designed to assess a student's level of phonological and phonemic awareness. These tests assess important phonological and phonemic awareness skills, including sound matching, sound isolation, sound blending, sound segmenting, sound deletion, and sound substitution. See page T22 for a more detailed description of the Phonological Awareness Inventory.

Progress-Monitoring Assessments Overview

The Progress-Monitoring Assessments provide biweekly checks on students' progress. These oral reading tests are administered individually and assess students' growth or problems in pre-reading/reading skills throughout the school year. In Kindergarten, these assessments provide checks on students' beginning reading skills as they progress from letter sounds to decoding words and reading high-frequency words and sentences. In Grade 1, these assessments provide checks on students' ability to decode words and read high-frequency words and sentences and culminate with Oral Reading Fluency passages. In Grades 2–6, there are grade-level biweekly Oral Reading Fluency passages. See page T25–T35 for a more detailed description of the Progress-Monitoring Assessments by grade level.

Administering and Scoring the Assessments

General Guidelines for Administering

The assessments must be administered individually as the items require oral responses. Following these general guidelines and directions when administering the assessments will help provide a positive testing atmosphere for both you and the student.

- Find a quiet setting in which to administer the assessments. This will enhance the student's concentration and make it easier to hear the student's responses.

- You and the student should be seated at a flat table or desk. The best seating location for you is facing the student to facilitate clear diction and immediate recording of responses.

- Become familiar with the directions and items. You should feel free to rephrase the directions, to repeat the samples, or to give additional examples to make sure the student understands what to do.

- Starting at the beginning of each assessment, guide the student through each subtest. Record his or her responses on the Recording Form.

- If the student becomes frustrated and unable to respond, stop the assessment.

- If you are administering a timed section, have a stopwatch or a clock with a second hand available to time the student's reading.

- Don't score or analyze the assessment in front of the student. Wait to do that until after the student has left.

General Directions

- Duplicate a copy of the Recording Form for each task you will be administering. You will record an individual student's responses on the Recording Form. When the task requires, the student will need a copy of the administration page for the particular task you are administering.

- Before starting each test, explain briefly that for most tests the student has a page and you have a page. You will be making notes so you can help him or her become a better reader.

- Do not provide any help with test items or tell the student whether answers are wrong or right.

- Be sure to speak clearly.

Administering and Scoring the Assessments

Screening Assessments

Letter-Naming Fluency

The Letter-Naming subtests for Kindergarten and Grade 1 are individually-administered tasks that assess a student's facility at naming uppercase or lowercase letters. The teacher points to individual letters, and the student names the letter. A stopwatch or clock with a second hand is required for this test.

Directions Explain that you want the student to tell you the names of these uppercase or lowercase letters. Point to each letter for the student. Use Blackline Master page 3. The student will read each letter as you record responses and time the test for one minute.

Say: *What letter is this?*
If the student does not know a letter, wait three seconds and then point to the next letter. Move left to right across the rows of letters.
Note: You may point to the letter, or use index cards or an index card with a "window" cut in it to show one letter at a time.

Recording On Recording Form page 5, indicate correct responses with ✓. If a student gives an incorrect letter, record the letter the student gave. Write **0** if the student does not respond.

Discontinue Discontinue testing if a student is unable to identify any of the first ten uppercase or lowercase letters.

Scoring One point is awarded for each correctly identified letter name.

Interpretation Use the following chart to help you assess students' performance.

	Kindergarten		Grade 1	
	Beginning-of-Year	**Mid-Year**	**Beginning-of-Year**	**Mid-Year**
Goal	8 out of 26 letters in one minute	14 out of 26 letters in one minute	18 out of 26 letters in one minute	24 out of 26 letters in one minute

A student's ability to learn letter names has long been associated with success in beginning reading. Knowing letter names is necessary to follow classroom directions, and many letter names are a clue to learning letter sounds. Most end-of-Kindergarten and beginning-of-Grade 1 students are able to correctly identify 24 out of 26 letters. Administer the Diagnostic Assessments: Print Concepts Inventory to students who struggle on the Letter-Naming Fluency assessment to determine whether they would benefit from additional Print Concepts instruction.

Phoneme Segmentation

The Phoneme Segmentation test for Kindergarten and Grade 1 is an individually-administered task that assesses a student's facility at listening to a word and producing each phoneme in the word.

Directions The teacher will follow the *Task, Model,* and *Sample* script on each form.

Recording On Administering and Recording Form page 6, indicate correct responses with ✓. If a student gives an incorrect sound, record the sound the student gave. If a student tells you the name of the letter, remind him or her that you want to know the sound. Write **0** if the student does not respond.

Discontinue Discontinue testing if a student is unable to identify any of the first three word sounds or if the student becomes frustrated.

Scoring Score one point for each correct response. There is only one correct response for each item, and the student must give all three or four phonemes.

Interpretation Use the following chart to help you assess students' performance.

	Kindergarten		Grade 1	
	Beginning-of-Year	**Mid-Year**	**Beginning-of-Year**	**Mid-Year**
Goal	4 out of 10 correct	6 out of 10 correct	6 out of 10 correct	8 out of 10 correct

A student's ability to identify the letter sounds in words is also associated with success in beginning reading. Administer the Diagnostic Assessments: Phonological Awareness Inventory to students who struggle on the Phoneme Segmentation assessment to determine whether they would benefit from additional Phonological Awareness instruction.

Nonsense-Word Reading

The Nonsense-Word Reading subtests for Grade 1 are individually-administered tasks that assess a student's knowledge of basic phonic patterns (CVC, CVCe, consonant blends and digraphs, and final double consonants) using pseudo or made-up words.

Directions Explain that you want the student to read these nonsense words to you. Point to each word for the student. Use Blackline Masters pages 7–9.

Say: *Read these made-up words aloud. These are not real words, so they won't make sense. Use what you know about the sounds that letters stand for to try to say these made-up words. What is this word?*
If the student does not know a word, wait approximately ten seconds and then point to the word. If there is no response, say: *Please make a try. What do you think this word might be?* If there is still no response, discontinue the test.

Recording On Recording Form page 10, indicate correct responses with ✓. If a student gives an incorrect sound, record the sound given. Write **0** if the student does not respond.

Discontinue Discontinue testing after five consecutive incorrect responses, failure to respond, or a combination of both.

Scoring One point is awarded for each item that is correctly identified.

Interpretation Use the following chart to help you assess students' performance.

	Grade 1	
	Beginning-of-Year	**Mid-Year**
Goal	6 out of 10 correct	8 out of 10 correct

A student's ability to apply knowledge of letter-sound correspondence is an important part of moving toward reading fluently. A score of eight out of ten for each test shows that the student has competent letter-sound correspondence for that pattern skill. Administer the Diagnostic Assessments: Letter-Sound Fluency tests to students who struggle on the Nonsense-Word Reading assessments to determine whether they would benefit from additional letter-sound instruction.

Word Identification

The Word Identification subtests for Grades 1 and 2 are individually-administered tasks that assess a student's knowledge of high-frequency and multisyllabic words.

Directions Explain that you want the student to read the words to you. Point to each word for the student on the student form. For Grade 1, see Blackline Masters pages 11–12; for Grade 2, see Blackline Masters pages 17–18.

Say: *Try to read these words aloud. What is this word?*
If the student does not know a word, wait approximately ten seconds and then point to the word. If there is no response, say: *Please make a try. What do you think this word might be?* If there is still no response, discontinue the test.

Recording On the recording form, indicate correct responses with ✓. If a student gives an incorrect word, record the word given. If nonsense words or individual sounds are given, represent what the student said phonetically. Write **0** if the student does not respond. For Grade 1, see Recording Form page 13; for Grade 2, see Recording Form page 19.

Discontinue Discontinue testing after five consecutive incorrect responses, failure to respond, or a combination of both.

Scoring One point is awarded for each item that is correctly identified.

Interpretation Use the following chart to help you assess students' performance.

	Grade 1		Grade 2
	Beginning-of-Year	**Mid-Year**	**Beginning-of-Year**
Goal	6 out of 10 correct	8 out of 10 correct	8 out of 10 correct

These words are among the most frequently used words in the English language. Learning these words is an important part of moving toward reading fluently. Administer the Screening Assessments: Nonsense-Word Reading tests to students who struggle on the Word Identification assessment to determine whether they would benefit from additional letter-sound instruction or testing.

Oral Reading Fluency

These Oral Reading passages are sequenced from a beginning-of-Grade 1 through a beginning-of-Grade 6 reading level. Individually, students will read a passage aloud while you note errors. Each test should take up to two minutes. A stopwatch or clock with a second hand is required for this test.

Directions Explain that there are two forms to this test—one for the student to read aloud and one for the teacher to record student fluency. The student will read the passage as you record errors and time the test for one minute. Mark an **X** on the last word that the student read at one minute. Allow the student to read the entire passage. Use the Blackline Masters for each grade level.

Say: *Read the following passage aloud. Read it as well as you can. I cannot help, so if you come to a word you don't know, just try your best. After you read, I will ask you to retell the passage in your own words.* If the student stops at a word and does not continue, wait approximately five seconds and then prompt by **saying**: *Please try to go on.* Do not supply the word.

After the reading, ask the student to retell the passage in his or her own words.

Recording Carefully track the oral reading and record any errors and self-corrections on the recording form.

- Mark any misread word.
- Mark any left-out word.
- Mark any extra words inserted.
- Mark any self-corrections over the error mark (suggested mark **SC**).

All errors, whether they change the meaning or not, are counted as errors. Repetitions and self-corrections are *not* counted as errors. If the student self-corrects, the original error is not counted. If the student repeats the same error, count the error only once; for example, if the student repeatedly misreads *have* as *had*, count that as only one error.

Discontinue If the student reads fewer than two of the first ten words, ask the student to stop. Write *discontinue* on the test form and a zero as the score.

Scoring: WCPM For older, more fluent readers, teachers calculate the *oral reading accuracy* score, which indicates the percentage of words the student reads correctly and is one measure of fluency. The reading rate is assessed by calculating words correct per minute, or WCPM.

For emergent readers, such as in Grade 1, who are not yet reading fluently, scores should be interpreted cautiously. A review of the *patterns* among a student's errors, though, gives especially useful information.

Note the total number of words that is given for the passage on the Recording Form. Below it, record the total number of errors. Compare the numbers to get a sense of the student's reading accuracy. (If you wish to convert to a percentage score, subtract errors from the total. Divide the result by the total words and then multiply by 100.)

Calculate Words Correct per Minute (WCPM)

- Count mispronunciations, additions, and omissions as errors. Do not count repetitions or self-corrections as errors.

- Subtract errors from total number of words read to get the total number of words read correctly in one minute (WCPM).

- After determining the student's fluency score, record it on the teacher's test form.

Scoring: Retelling Have the student retell the passage. Take notes and mark the score on the Summary Recording Form.

Comprehension: Retelling Rubric

Score	Description
2 (Goal)	• Includes the main idea or problem, significant events or information, supporting details • Retelling is organized in sequence and is coherent
1	• Retelling is unfocused, not detailed, or requires prompting
0	• If student cannot or did not respond

Interpretation Use the following chart to help you assess students' WCPM performance.

	Goal (WCPM)		Goal (WCPM)
Grade 1 (Mid-Year)	13–33	Grade 4	84–104
Grade 2	41–61	Grade 5	100–120
Grade 3	61–81	Grade 6	117–137

Source: Hasbrouck, Jan, and Gerald A. Tindal. 2006. Oral reading fluency norms: A valuable assessment tool for reading teachers. Reading Teacher 59 (April), no. 7: 636–644.

- Fluency goals are based on grade-level norms to measure a student's fluency ability. Review the patterns in the student's oral reading errors to help you identify instructional needs and plan specific support. Administer the Screening Assessments: Word Identification tests to students who struggle on the Oral Reading Fluency assessment to determine whether they would benefit from additional high-frequency word instruction, letter-sound instruction, or testing. For students who score below Goal on Retelling, emphasize understanding the meaning of text. Take turns with the student modeling how to apply comprehension strategies to different texts.

Diagnostic Assessments

Print Concepts Inventory

The Print Concepts Inventory is an individually-administered inventory designed for students who have not yet learned to read independently. This test may be administered three times during the school year to monitor a student's developing familiarity with books and written language. The Print Concepts Inventory test can be administered throughout the year to monitor a student's progress.

Directions

Parts of a Book Select a short picture book with pictures at the top of each page and several lines of text at the bottom. Hand the book to the student in a vertical position with the spine facing the student. Use the book for items 1–6. Record the student's score on the Print Concepts Inventory Recording Form page 35.

1. **Say:** *Where is the front of the book?*
2. **Say:** *Where is the back of the book?*
3. **Say:** *Where is the title page of the book? Show me where you would find the title page in the book.*
4. **Say:** *Where is the title of the book?*
5. **Say:** *What is an author? What does he or she do?*
6. **Say:** *What is an illustrator? What does he or she do?*

Purpose of Print Use Blackline Master page 33 for items 7–14 and use Blackline Master page 34 for items 15–25. Explain that you are going to ask students to find some things on this page.

Practice Item: Say: *Which of these is a square?* Point to the square, if necessary.

Directions: Provide no additional help as you state each direction.

7. **Say:** *What is a number? Show me which of these is a number standing all by itself.*

8. **Say:** *What is a letter? Show me which of these is a letter standing all by itself—just one letter by itself.*

9. **Say:** *What is a word? Show me which of these is a word standing all by itself—just one word by itself.*

10. Point to the word, *Cat.* **Say:** *Where is the first letter of this word? Show me which is the first letter in this word.*

11. Point to the word, *Cat.* **Say:** *Where is the last letter of this word? Show me which is the last letter in this word.*

12. **Say:** *What is a sentence? Show me which of these is a sentence.*

13–14. With your finger, draw an oval around the sentence. **Say:** *This sentence says,* A girl found a red ball. *I'm going to read the words again slowly. I want you to touch each of the words in the sentence with your finger as I say the words. Point your finger to the first word in this sentence* (Have the student point to the first word.) *Now move your finger to show the word I'm reading.* (Read each word slowly as you continue reading the sentence. Determine that the student understands that there are spaces between each word.)

Now use Blackline Master page 34 for items 15–25. Explain that you are going to use this page for some additional questions.

15. With your finger, draw an oval around the title and sentences at the top of the form. **Say:** *Point your finger to the title.*

16. With your finger, point to the first sentence (directly under the title) at the top of the form. **Say:** *Point your finger to show which word I would start with if I was going to read this sentence.*

17. With your finger, draw an oval around all of the sentences. **Say:** *Point your finger to show which way I would go if I were reading these sentences.* The student should point left to right. (If the student stops at the end of the sentence, ask question 18; if not, go to question 20.)

18. Point your finger to the end of the first sentence. **Say:** *Where do I go when I reach this place in a sentence? Point your finger to show where I would go next to continue reading.* The student should indicate a return sweep.

19. **Say:** *Slide your finger along the words to show where I would go to finish reading all of these sentences.* The student should continue to the bottom of the passage (from top to bottom).

20. With your finger, point to the first sentence. **Say:** *Point your finger to show which word in this sentence begins with a capital letter/uppercase letter.*

21. Point to the period at the end of the first sentence. **Say:** *What is this? What is it for?* The student should identify the period as something that ends a sentence.

22. Point to the question mark at the end of the last sentence. **Say:** *What is this? What is it for?* The student should identify the question mark as something that comes at the end of a question.

23. With your finger, point to the second sentence. **Say:** *Point your finger to show me an exclamation mark.*

24. Point to the word *like* in the second sentence. **Say:** *This is the word* like. *Look at the next sentences to find the word* like *repeated.*

25. Point to the first pair of words. **Say:** *Look at these two words. One of them is the word* won *and the other is the word* wonderful. *Which of these words is* won? Use the same directions, alternating long and short words as the target items for following word pairs *in, introduction; tell, television;* and *Chris, chrysanthemums.*

Recording On Recording Form page 35, indicate correct responses with ✓. Write **0** if the student does not respond.

Discontinue In the Parts of a Book section, discontinue if a student misses four of the first six items. In the Purpose of Print section, discontinue if the student misses four answers in a row or if the student becomes frustrated.

Scoring Score one point for each of the items in 1–24. To score the "tracking" of print in items 15–23 as correct, there should be clear evidence from the behavior of the student that he or she understands that each spoken word is represented by a printed word. Item 25 (Spoken/Written Word Correspondence) has four examples to reduce the effects of guessing a correct response. If a student gets at least three of the four items correct, give credit for knowing that a longer spoken word (one with more syllables) is represented by a longer printed word.

Interpretation It is important that students understand fundamental concepts such as what is meant by a word, a letter, and a sentence. These concepts seem to be fairly easy skills for most end-of-kindergarten students. Provide additional print concepts instruction for students who struggle on the Print Concepts Inventory.

Goals for Interpreting the Concepts of Print Inventory for Kindergarten

Total Score	Performance Level	Instructional Description and Recommendations
1–13	Minimal Understanding	A student at this level has a very limited understanding of books and Print Concepts. A student at this level could profit from activities such as: • listening to stories • talking about books • oral language activities • language experience or diction activities
14–20	Emerging Understanding	A student at this level has a moderate understanding of books and Print Concepts. A student at this level could profit from activities such as: • following along as others read a story • reading pattern books with an adult reader • playing rhyming games and other oral language games • language experience or diction activities
21–28	Developed Understanding (Goal)	A student at this level demonstrates an excellent understanding of the fundamental Print Concepts. A student at this level could profit from activities such as: • reading pattern books with an adult reader • following in print while a teacher or parent reads orally • interacting with a teacher or parent about the content of a story read orally • drawing and writing about things or events that are meaningful

Letter-Sound Fluency

The Letter-Sound Fluency subtest is an individually-administered task that assesses the student's ability to associate letters with sounds. The teacher points to a letter, and the student makes the sound associated with the letter.

Directions Explain that you want to see how fast the student can tell you the sounds of these letters. Be sure to speak clearly. Use the Blackline Master on page 37.

Point to each letter for the student. If the student tells you the letter name, repeat that you want to know what *sound* the letter makes. If the student gives an alternative sound, ask whether there is another sound that letter makes. If the student does not know a letter sound, wait three seconds and then point to the next letter. Use a stopwatch or second hand to time the task.

Calculate Letter-Sounds Correct per Minute

- Count mispronunciations as errors. Do not count self-corrections as errors.

- Subtract errors from total number of words read to get the total number of letter-sounds identified correctly in one minute.

- After determining the student's fluency score, record it on the teacher's test form.

Recording On Recording Form page 38, indicate correct responses with ✓. If a student gives an incorrect sound, record the sound given. Write **0** if the student does not respond.

Discontinue Discontinue testing after five consecutive incorrect responses, failure to respond, or a combination of both.

Scoring Total the number of letter sounds correctly identified by the student. This is the accuracy score.

Interpretation Compare the student's accuracy score and rate with the goals found on the next page. Students who meet or exceed the goal can be considered at or above grade level for the time of year the subtest was administered. Students who score below this require additional instruction in letter-sound relationships.

Total Score	Performance Level	Instructional Description and Recommendations
Identified 7–8 letter sounds in one minute	Minimal Understanding	A student at this level has a very limited understanding of letter-sounds. A student at this level could profit from activities such as: • letter-sound identification activities • letter-sound fluency activities • oral language activities • language experience or diction activities
Identified 13–20 letter sounds in one minute	Emerging Understanding	A student at this level has a moderate understanding of letter-sounds. A student at this level could profit from activities such as: • letter-sound fluency activities • oral language activities • playing oral language games • language experience or diction activities
Identified 22–26 letter sounds in one minute	Developed Understanding (Goal)	A student at this level demonstrates an excellent understanding of letter-sounds. A student at this level could profit from activities such as: • blending syllables • identifying and blending phonemes • interacting with a teacher or parent to read and decode words orally

Phonological Awareness Inventory

The Phonological Awareness Inventory consists of a series of individually-administered oral tests designed to assess a student's level of phonological and phonemic awareness. They assess important phonological and phonemic awareness skills, including sound matching, sound isolation, sound blending, sound segmenting, sound deletion, and sound substitution. Below are detailed descriptions of the Phonological Awareness Inventory assessments.

Words in a Sentence Assesses a student's ability to identify the number of words in a sentence

Blend Syllables Assesses a student's ability to blend individual syllables to produce a word

Segment Syllables Assesses a student's ability to identify the number of syllables in a word

Delete Syllables Assesses a student's ability to delete a syllable to produce a new word

Recognize Rhyming Words Assesses a student's ability to recognize words that rhyme

Produce Rhyming Words Assesses a student's ability to produce a word that rhymes with another word

Categorize Rhyming Words Assesses a student's ability to categorize rhyming words by identifying which word does not rhyme with a series of other words

Blend Onset and Rime Assesses a student's ability to blend word families to produce a word

Segment Onset and Rime Assesses a student's ability to delete a sound in a word to create a new word

Isolate Initial Sound Assesses a student's ability to listen to a word and isolate the beginning sound of that word

Isolate Final Sound Assesses a student's ability to listen to a word and isolate the ending sound of that word

Isolate Medial Sound Assesses a student's ability to listen to a word and isolate the middle sound of that word

Identify Phonemes Assesses a student's ability to identify the initial phoneme that is the same between words

Categorize Phonemes Assesses a student's ability to identify the initial phoneme that is different from other words

Blend Phonemes Assesses a student's ability to blend sounds together to say the word

Segment Phonemes Assesses a student's ability to identify the individual sounds in a spoken word

Delete Phonemes Assesses a student's ability to delete an individual phoneme in a word and orally produce the remaining part of the word

Add Phonemes Assesses a student's ability to add an individual phoneme to a word and orally produce the new word

Substitute Phonemes Assesses a student's ability to substitute either the initial or final sound in a spoken word to produce a new word

Administration of the Phonological Awareness Inventory Assessments

- The Phonological Awareness Inventories cover a broad range of skills. Some of the skills, such as identifying the number of words in a simple sentence, can be performed by many beginning Kindergarten students. Other skills, however, such as substituting initial and final sounds, are not usually performed by students until the end of Kindergarten or the beginning of Grade 1. Therefore, be cautious about asking students to perform tasks beyond their developmental level. **If a student misses four items in a row, discontinue testing of that particular task and move on to the next task. Stop testing any time a student displays frustration with or is unable to perform a task.**

- The Phonological Awareness Inventories should be conducted individually in a quiet and comfortable setting. By administering an inventory individually, the teacher can be sure the student is attending to the task and can gain insights into problems the student may be having.

- You and the student should be seated at a flat table or desk. Face the student to facilitate clear diction and immediate recording of responses.

- Become familiar with the directions and items. You should feel free to rephrase the directions, to repeat the samples, or to give additional examples to make sure the student understands what to do.

- Before beginning an inventory, spend a few minutes in light, friendly conversation with the student. Don't refer to the inventory as a "test." Tell the student you would like to play some "word games."

Specific Directions for Administration

1. Duplicate a copy of the Administering and Recording Form for each task you will be administering. These forms can be found in the Blackline Masters of this book. You will record a student's responses on the Administering and Recording Form. The student will not need any materials.

2. Explain that the words a student hears and says every day are made up of sounds and that you will be saying some words and sounds and asking questions about them. Be sure to speak clearly.

3. Administer the tasks in sequential order. If the student has difficulty with the first four items or cannot answer them, stop giving that particular task and move on to another.

4. Follow the same basic procedures when administering each task. First, model the task so the student understands what to do. Second, administer the sample item and provide positive feedback to the student. Third, administer the items for that task. Fourth, record the student's responses for each item.

Scoring and Interpreting the Results

After giving an inventory, record the student's scores on the Summary Recording Form. Use the goals on the Summary Recording Form to determine the level that best describes the student's phonological and phonemic awareness. Students who score below the goal likely require additional phonological and phonemic awareness instruction. Students whose scores are at or above the goal do not need additional phonological and phonemic awareness instruction in the evaluated areas. To inform instruction, indicate observations from specific tasks, especially for those areas where the student had obvious difficulty with the task or required additional prompting.

Progress-Monitoring Assessments: Kindergarten

Administer each assessment orally to individual students approximately every two weeks. The test should take three to five minutes. Prepare one student test form and a teacher's test form for each student being tested. Use the teacher's test form to record the student's responses and scores.

Keep in Mind

- Find a quiet place to give the test.

- Seat the student on the opposite side of a desk or table so that you can record responses inconspicuously.

- Tell the student that you want to learn how well he or she understands new sounds and words that the group has been learning. Explain that you will write down the student's responses to help you remember them.

- Check to be sure the student is on the right row or word.

- Give directions for each section, modifying them so that the student understands what to do.

- Give the student a reasonable time to respond.

- Stop testing if the student becomes frustrated or is unable to respond. If a student misses four responses in a row in a skills area, stop testing and go on to the next skills area.

- Wait to score or analyze responses until the student has left.

Directions Explain briefly that the student has a page and you have a page. You will be making notes so you can help him or her become a better reader.

Recording Use your page to record the student's oral responses. For most tests, indicate correct responses with _✓_. Write the incorrect response or an **X**. Write **0** if the student does not respond.

Discontinue Discontinue testing after four consecutive incorrect responses, failure to respond, or a combination of both.

Phonemic Awareness Read the teacher directions on the teacher page. Be sure the student is listening as directions are given. Check goals and enter the number of correct responses.

Letter-Naming Point to the box with the letters. Point to a capital or lowercase letter and ask the student to name the letter. Continue with the other letters in the box. Check goals and enter the number of correct responses.

Letter-Sound Relationships Tell the student to look at the letters. Then read the directions provided on the teacher page. Check goals and enter the number of correct responses.

High-Frequency Words Point to the test box and tell the student that he or she has learned the words. Then point to each word and have the student read it. Enter the number of correct responses on the score line.

Decodable Words Have the student look at the words. Remind the student that he or she knows the sounds for all the letters in each word. Have the student identify each word by sounding out and blending the word. Enter the number of correct responses.

Sentence Reading Tell the student that he or she will read each sentence. Have the student look at the sentence and read the words. Some sentences have a picture for a word. Tell the student to read the name of the picture with the other words in the sentence. The student may take time to sound out a word or words. If the student goes back to correct an error, the response is correct. Check goals and enter the student's score.

Scoring Obtain a student's raw score for each section by determining the number of correct answers or words read correctly; record the score on the teacher's test form. Treat each word or letter as a separate item. Count mispronunciations, additions, and omissions as errors. Do not count repetitions or self-corrections as errors. Record the number of words or letters read correctly.

Use the student's scores to determine whether the student is meeting the goals that are given for each section. Use the test data and your observations to decide whether the student should move ahead or needs reteaching. Record each student's scores across assessment periods on the Summary Recording Forms. See the Blackline Masters on pages S3–S6.

Interpretation Use Progress-Monitoring Assessment results, core instruction assessments, and your professional judgment to make decisions about future intervention instruction. They will help you:

- determine whether the student needs additional intervention or can be transitioned back to core instruction only

- evaluate the overall effectiveness of intervention by noting sufficient progress and learning

- adjust skill instruction to address specific learning gaps

Consider how a student's score compares with the section goals. Decide whether the student is benefiting from additional intervention.

Adjusting Instruction Analyze a student's errors and self-corrections in each section to identify problem areas and a starting point for reteaching, review, and extra practice.

- For phonics errors, provide additional word-blending activities using word lists that feature target phonics skills.

- For errors in recognizing high-frequency words, supply brief cumulative lists (approximately ten words) of high-frequency words to read and reread with increasing speed and accuracy.

If some students are not meeting the goals of the Progress-Monitoring tests or the assessments in the core instructional program, it may indicate the need for additional testing and more intensive intervention.

Progress-Monitoring Assessments: Grade 1

Administer each assessment orally to individual students approximately every two weeks. The test should take three to five minutes. Prepare one student test form and a teacher's test form for each student being tested. Use the teacher's test form to record the student's responses and scores.

Keep in Mind

- Find a quiet area to conduct the test.

- Explain the task and let the student know that you will be taking notes as he or she answers or reads a passage aloud.

- Tell the student to answer or read at his or her usual pace and to not rush through the words or sentences.

- Wait until the student has left to score and analyze the results.

High-Frequency Words Point to the test box and tell the student that he or she has learned the words. Then point to each word and have the student read it. If the word is misread, write what the student said above the word. Treat each word as a separate item. Enter the number of correct responses on the score line.

Decodable Words Point to each word. Allow time for the student to look at the words. Have the student read each word by sounding out and blending the word. If the word is misread, write what the student said above the word. Treat each word as a separate item. Enter the number of correct responses.

Reading Sentences Tell the student that he or she will read each sentence. Have the student look at the sentence and read the words. If a word is misread, write what the student said above the word. Draw a line through any words that are skipped and insert words that the student adds. Mark self-corrections with an **SC** above the word(s) for your records. Treat each word in the sentence as a separate item. Enter the number of correct responses on the score line.

Oral Reading Fluency

Have a clock or watch with a second hand or a stopwatch available to time the student's reading.

Directions Explain that there are two forms to this test—one for the student to read aloud and one for the teacher to record student fluency. The student will read the passage as you record errors and time the test for one minute. Mark an **X** on the last word that the student read at one minute. Allow the student to read the entire passage. Use the Blackline Masters beginning on page 111.

Say: *Read the following passage aloud. Read it as best as you can. I cannot help, so if you come to a word you don't know, just try your best. After you read, I will ask you to retell the passage in your own words.* If the student stops at a word and does not continue, wait approximately five seconds and then prompt by **saying**: *Please try to go on.* Do not supply the word.

After the reading, ask the student to retell the passage in his or her own words.

Recording Carefully track the oral reading and record any errors and self-corrections on the recording forms.

- Mark any misread word.

- Mark any left-out word.

- Mark any extra words inserted.

- Mark any self-corrections over the error mark (suggested mark **SC**).

All errors, whether they change the meaning or not, are counted as errors. Repetitions and self-corrections are *not* counted as errors. If the student self-corrects, the original error is not counted. If the student repeats the same error, count the error only once; for example, if the student repeatedly misreads *have* as *had*, count that as only one error.

Discontinue If the student reads fewer than two of the first ten words, ask the student to stop. Write *discontinue* on the test form and a zero as the score.

Scoring: WCPM Obtain a student's raw score for each section by determining the number of words read correctly; record the score on the teacher's test form.

To determine accuracy scores

- Treat each word as a separate item.

- Count mispronunciations, additions, and omissions as errors.

- Do not count repetitions or self-corrections as errors.

- Record the number of words read correctly.

To score fluency for oral reading passages

- Determine errors made in reading for one minute, using the guidelines for accuracy above.

- Determine words read correctly in one minute by subtracting from the total words read.

- The reading rate is assessed by calculating words correct per minute, or WCPM.

Calculate Words Correct per Minute (WCPM)

- Count mispronunciations, additions, and omissions as errors. Do not count repetitions or self-corrections as errors.

- Subtract errors from total number of words read to get the total number of words read correctly in one minute (WCPM).

- After determining the student's fluency score, record it on the teacher's test form.

Scoring: Retelling Have the student retell the passage. Take notes and mark the score on the Summary Recording Form.

Comprehension: Retelling Rubric

Score	Description
2 (Goal)	• Includes the main idea or problem, significant events or information, supporting details • Retelling is organized in sequence and is coherent
1	• Retelling is unfocused, not detailed, or requires prompting
0	• If student cannot or did not respond

Interpreting Test Results Use the following chart to help you assess students' WCPM performance.

Grade 1	Goal (WCPM)
Winter	13–33
Spring	43–63

Source: Hasbrouck, Jan, and Gerald A. Tindal. 2006. Oral reading fluency norms: A valuable assessment tool for reading teachers. Reading Teacher 59 (April), no. 7: 636–644.

Fluency goals are based on grade-level norms to measure a student's fluency ability. Review the patterns in the student's oral reading errors to help you identify instructional needs and plan specific support. Administer the Screening Assessments: Word Identification tests to students who struggle on the Oral Reading Fluency assessment to determine whether they would benefit from additional high-frequency word instruction, letter-sound instruction, or testing. For students who score below Goal on Retelling, emphasize understanding the meaning of text. Take turns with student modeling how to apply comprehension strategies to different texts.

Adjusting Instruction Analyze a student's errors and self-corrections in each section to identify problem areas and a starting point for reteaching, review, and extra practice.

• For decoding errors, provide additional word-blending activities using word lists that feature target phonics skills. The goal here is for the student to be able to read approximately one word per second.

• For errors in recognizing high-frequency words, supply brief cumulative lists (approximately ten words) of high-frequency words to read and reread with increasing speed and accuracy.

• For improving rate, provide texts at a student's independent reading level for repeated or coached readings.

Progress-Monitoring Assessments: Grades 2–6

Administer each assessment orally to individual students approximately every two weeks. The test should take three to five minutes. Prepare one student test form and a teacher's test form for each student being tested. Use the teacher's test form to record the student's responses and scores.

Keep in Mind

- Find a quiet area to conduct the test.

- Explain the task and let the student know that you will be taking notes as he or she reads a passage aloud.

- Tell the student to read at his or her usual pace and to not rush through the passage.

- Wait until the student has left to score and analyze the results.

Oral Reading Fluency

Have a clock or watch with a second hand or a stopwatch available to time the student's reading.

Directions Explain that there are two forms to this test—one for the student to read aloud and one for the teacher to record student fluency. The student will read the passage as you record errors and time the test for one minute. Mark an **X** on the last word that the student read at one minute. Allow the student to read the entire passage. Use the Blackline Masters to administer these grade-level tests.

Say: *Read the following passage aloud. Read it as best as you can. I cannot help, so if you come to a word you don't know, just try your best. After you read, I will ask you to retell the passage in your own words.* If the student stops at a word and does not continue, wait approximately five seconds and then prompt by **saying:** *Please try to go on.* Do not supply the word.

After the reading, ask the student to retell the passage in his or her own words.

Recording Carefully track the oral reading and record any errors and self-corrections on the recording forms.

- Mark any misread word.

- Mark any left-out word.

- Mark any extra words inserted.

- Mark any self-corrections over the error mark (suggested mark **SC**).

All errors, whether they change the meaning or not, are counted as errors. Repetitions and self-corrections are *not* counted as errors. If the student self-corrects, the original error is not counted. If the student repeats the same error, count the error only once; for example, if the student repeatedly misreads *have* as *had*, count that as only one error.

Discontinue If the student reads fewer than two of the first ten words, ask the student to stop. Write *discontinue* on the test form and a zero as the score.

Scoring: WCPM Obtain a student's raw score for each section by determining the number of words read correctly; record the score on the teacher's test form.

To determine accuracy scores

- Treat each word as a separate item.

- Count mispronunciations, additions, and omissions as errors.

- Do not count repetitions or self-corrections as errors.

- Record the number of words read correctly.

To score fluency for oral reading passages

- Determine errors made in reading for one minute, using the guidelines for accuracy above.

- Determine words read correctly in one minute by subtracting from the total words read.

The reading rate is assessed by calculating words correct per minute, or WCPM.

Calculate Words Correct per Minute (WCPM)

- Count mispronunciations, additions, and omissions as errors. Do not count repetitions or self-corrections as errors.

- Subtract errors from total number of words read to get the total number of words read correctly in one minute (WCPM).

- After determining the student's fluency score, record it on the teacher's test form.

Scoring: Retelling Have the student retell the passage. Take notes and mark the score on the Summary Recording Form.

Comprehension: Retelling Rubric

Score	Description
2 (Goal)	• Includes the main idea or problem, significant events or information, supporting details • Retelling is organized in sequence and is coherent
1	• May include the main idea or problem, most significant events, some details • Retelling is generally organized and sequenced, may have some misinformation
0	• Retelling is unfocused, not detailed, or requires prompting • If student cannot or did not respond

Interpreting Test Results Use the following chart to help you assess students' WCPM performance.

Words Correct Per Minute

	Beginning of Year	Mid-year	End of Year
Grade 1		13–33	43–63
Grade 2	41–61	62–82	79–99
Grade 3	61–81	82–102	97–117
Grade 4	84–104	102–122	113–133
Grade 5	100–120	117–137	129–149
Grade 6	117–137	130–150	140–160

*WCPM = Words Correct per Minute

- Fluency goals are based on grade-level norms to measure a student's fluency ability. Review the patterns in the student's oral reading errors to help you identify instructional needs and plan specific support.

- In the lower grades, administer the Screening Assessments: Word Identification tests to students who struggle on the Oral Reading Fluency assessment to determine whether they would benefit from additional high-frequency word instruction, letter-sound instruction, or testing.

- In the upper grades, reteach the phonics/decoding skills as needed, and provide appropriate word lists for more practice. If a student is making many self-corrections, try recording the student's reading and play it back so he or she can hear his or her own reading. Provide familiar texts at a student's independent reading level for repeated or coached readings.

- For students who score below Goal on Retelling, emphasize understanding the meaning of text. Take turns with student modeling how to apply comprehension strategies to different texts.

Adjusting Instruction Analyze a student's errors and self-corrections in each section to identify problem areas and a starting point for reteaching, review, and extra practice. For improving rate, provide texts at a student's independent reading level for repeated or coached readings.

Recommendations for Data-Driven Instruction

The measures in *Intervention Assessments* are designed to inform instruction. Consult the Summary Recording Form for each student, and follow the recommendations below. As always, take into account your professional judgment, classroom observations, and the results of other assessments.

Overview

Use these steps to ensure you are providing data-driven intervention:

1. **IDENTIFY STUDENT NEEDS** If a student shows a weak area on the Screening Assessment, administer a more specific, diagnostic test to pinpoint the missing skills.

2. **TEACH TO THE NEED** Provide intensive instruction based on assessment results, using *HMH Decoding Power: Intensive Reading Instruction*.

3. **SCAFFOLD THE CORE** In addition, continue providing scaffolded support (which may include strategic, or Tier II, intervention) during core instruction, for two weeks.

4. **MONITOR PROGRESS** Monitor progress using the Progress-Monitoring Assessments and core assessments.

5. **IF NECESSARY, PROBLEM-SOLVE WITH COLLEAGUES** If students are not catching up, you may need to readminister the Screening Assessment or a different screening or diagnostic instrument. If the student is an English learner, be sure to assess in his or her native language, if possible. Consult with other teammates or specialists in your district as required.

Recommendations in Detail:
Kindergarten

Screening Assessments*	IF "Below Goal" on Screening Assessment, THEN
Letter-Naming Fluency	1. IDENTIFY STUDENT NEEDS Administer **Diagnostic Assessment:** Print Concepts Inventory to identify missing skills and knowledge about print concepts. 2. TEACH TO THE NEED Administer the corresponding lessons in *HMH Decoding Power,* choosing from Sessions K.1–K.31. 3. SCAFFOLD THE CORE Provide scaffolded support, which may include small-group work and/or strategic intervention, to help students access core instruction. 4. MONITOR PROGRESS Monitor progress with **Progress-Monitoring Assessments** and core assessments.
Phoneme Segmentation	1. IDENTIFY STUDENT NEEDS Administer **Diagnostic Assessment:** Phonological Awareness Inventory. 2. TEACH TO THE NEED Administer the corresponding lessons in *HMH Decoding Power,* choosing from Sessions K.32–K.55. 3. SCAFFOLD THE CORE Provide scaffolded support, which may include small-group work and/or strategic intervention, to help students access core instruction. 4. MONITOR PROGRESS Monitor progress with **Progress-Monitoring Assessments** and core assessments.

*Note: You may want to make decisions about adapting instruction or providing intervention based on the Mid-Year Screening Assessment. The Beginning-of-Year Screening Assessment is often used to establish a baseline for tracking future growth.

Recommendations in Detail:
Grade 1

Screening Assessments	IF "Below Goal" on Screening Assessment, THEN
Letter-Naming Fluency	1. IDENTIFY STUDENT NEEDS Administer **Diagnostic Assessment:** Print Concepts Inventory to identify missing skills and knowledge about print concepts. 2. TEACH TO THE NEED Administer the corresponding lessons in *HMH Decoding Power*, choosing from Sessions K.1–K.31. 3. SCAFFOLD THE CORE Provide scaffolded support, which may include small-group work and/or strategic intervention, to help students access core instruction. 4. MONITOR PROGRESS Monitor progress with **Progress-Monitoring Assessments** and core assessments.
Phoneme Segmentation	1. IDENTIFY STUDENT NEEDS Administer **Diagnostic Assessment:** Phonological Awareness Inventory to identify missing skills and knowledge about phonological awareness. 2. TEACH TO THE NEED Administer the corresponding lessons in *HMH Decoding Power*, choosing from Sessions K.32–K.55. 3. SCAFFOLD THE CORE Provide scaffolded support, which may include small-group work and/or strategic intervention, to help students access core instruction. 4. MONITOR PROGRESS Monitor progress with **Progress-Monitoring Assessments** and core assessments.
Nonsense-Word Fluency	1. IDENTIFY STUDENT NEEDS Administer **Diagnostic Assessment:** Letter-Sound Fluency to identify missing skills and knowledge about phonic elements. 2. TEACH TO THE NEED Identify the phonic elements the student struggled with and administer those lessons in *HMH Decoding Power*, Sessions K.56–1.37. 3. SCAFFOLD THE CORE Provide scaffolded support, which may include small-group work and/or strategic intervention, to help students access core instruction. 4. MONITOR PROGRESS Monitor progress with **Progress-Monitoring Assessments** and core assessments.

Word Identification	1. **IDENTIFY STUDENT NEEDS** Administer Diagnostic Assessment: Letter-Sound Fluency to identify missing skills and knowledge about phonic elements.
	2. **TEACH TO THE NEED** Identify the high-frequency words and phonic elements the student struggled with and administer those lessons in HMH Decoding Power, Sessions K.56–1.37.
	3. **SCAFFOLD THE CORE** Provide scaffolded support, which may include small-group work and/or strategic intervention, to help students access core instruction.
	4. **MONITOR PROGRESS** Monitor progress with Progress-Monitoring Assessments and core assessments.
Oral Reading Fluency (Mid-Year only)	1. **IDENTIFY STUDENT NEEDS** Administer **Screening Assessments:** Nonsense Word Fluency and Word Identification.
	2. **TEACH TO THE NEED** Administer lessons in *HMH Decoding Power*, beginning with Session 1.1A.
	3. **SCAFFOLD THE CORE** Provide scaffolded support, which may include small-group work and/or strategic intervention, to help students access core instruction.
	4. **MONITOR PROGRESS** Monitor progress with **Progress-Monitoring Assessments** and core assessments.

Recommendations in Detail:
Grade 2

Screening Assessments	IF "Below Goal" on Screening Assessment, THEN
Word Identification	1. **IDENTIFY STUDENT NEEDS** Administer **Diagnostic Assessment:** Letter-Sound Fluency to identify missing skills and knowledge about phonic elements. 2. **TEACH TO THE NEED** Identify the high-frequency words and phonic elements the student struggled with and administer those lessons in *HMH Decoding Power*, Sessions K.56–2.36. 3. **SCAFFOLD THE CORE** Provide scaffolded support, which may include small-group work and/or strategic intervention, to help students access core instruction. 4. **MONITOR PROGRESS** Monitor progress with **Progress-Monitoring Assessments** and core assessments.
Oral Reading Fluency	1. **IDENTIFY STUDENT NEEDS** Administer prior grades' Screening Assessments, beginning with **G1 Screening Assessments:** Oral Reading Fluency. Follow prior grades' Recommendations in Detail as needed. 2. **TEACH TO THE NEED** If student scores "Above Goal" on prior grades' Screening Assessments, administer lessons in *HMH Decoding Power*, beginning with Session 2.1A. 3. **SCAFFOLD THE CORE** Provide scaffolded support, which may include small-group work and/or strategic intervention, to help students access core instruction. 4. **MONITOR PROGRESS** Monitor progress with **Progress-Monitoring Assessments** and core assessments.

Recommendations in Detail:
Grade 3

Screening Assessments	IF "Below Goal" on Screening Assessment, THEN
Oral Reading Fluency	1. **IDENTIFY STUDENT NEEDS** Administer prior grades' Screening Assessments, beginning with **G2 Screening Assessments:** Oral Reading Fluency. Follow prior grades' Recommendations in Detail as needed. 2. **TEACH TO THE NEED** If student scores "Above Goal" on prior grades' Screening Assessments, administer lessons in *HMH Decoding Power*, beginning with Session 3.1. 3. **SCAFFOLD THE CORE** Provide scaffolded support, which may include small-group work and/or strategic intervention, to help students access core instruction. 4. **MONITOR PROGRESS** Monitor progress with **Progress-Monitoring Assessments** and core assessments.

Recommendations in Detail:
Grades 4–6

Screening Assessments	IF "Below Goal" on Screening Assessment, THEN
Oral Reading Fluency	1. **IDENTIFY STUDENT NEEDS** Administer prior grades' Screening Assessments, beginning with the immediately prior grade's **Screening Assessments:** Oral Reading Fluency. Follow prior grades' Recommendations in Detail as needed. 2. **TEACH TO THE NEED** If student scores "Above Goal" on prior grades' Screening Assessments, administer lessons in *HMH Decoding Power*, beginning with Session 4–6.1. 3. **SCAFFOLD THE CORE** Provide scaffolded support, which may include small-group work and/or strategic intervention, to help students access core instruction. 4. **MONITOR PROGRESS** Monitor progress with **Progress-Monitoring Assessments** and core assessments.

Summary Recording Forms

A Note About the Summary Recording Forms

A Summary Recording form is provided for each grade level. Use this form to gather the scores from each assessment type and from the subtests of the assessments and to compare the student's progress with curriculum-based goals. You can also use this form to identify student trends in the classroom and to modify instruction.

Informing Parents About Student's Progress

You can use the Summary Recording forms from each assessment to communicate with parents about their student's progress. Fill out the form to let parents know the degree to which their student is mastering grade-level skills.

Kindergarten • Summary Recording Form

Name _____ Teacher _____ School year _____

Screening Assessments		Date Given	Score		Actions (Check One)	
			Goal	Student's Score	Meets Goals	Needs Intervention
Letter Naming Fluency Lowercase	Beginning-of-Year		8 out of 26 letters	___ / 26		
	Mid-Year		14 out of 26 letters	___ / 26		
Letter Naming Fluency Uppercase	Beginning-of-Year		8 out of 26 letters	___ / 26		
	Mid-Year		14 out of 26 letters	___ / 26		
Phoneme Segmentation	Beginning-of-Year		4 / 10	___ / 10		
	Mid-Year		6 / 10	___ / 10		

Diagnostic Assessments		Date Given	Score		Actions (Check One)	
			Goal	Student's Score	Meets Goals	Needs Intervention
Print Concepts	Beginning-of-Year		14 / 28	___ / 28		
	Mid-Year		21 / 28	___ / 28		
Letter Sound Fluency	Beginning-of-Year		13 / 20	___ / 20		
	Mid-Year		22 / 26	___ / 26		

Name _____ Teacher _____ School year _____

Diagnostic Assessments

Phonological Awareness Inventory	Date Given	Score		Actions (Check One)	
		Goal	Student's Score	Meets Goals	Needs Intervention
Words in a Sentence		8 / 10	___ / 10		
Blend Syllables		8 / 10	___ / 10		
Segment Syllables		8 / 10	___ / 10		
Delete Syllables		8 / 10	___ / 10		
Recognize Rhyming Words		8 / 10	___ / 10		
Produce Rhyming Words		8 / 10	___ / 10		
Categorize Rhyming Words		4 / 5	___ / 5		
Blend Onset and Rime		8 / 10	___ / 10		
Segment Onset and Rime		8 / 10	___ / 10		
Isolate Initial Sounds		8 / 10	___ / 10		
Isolate Final Sounds		8 / 10	___ / 10		
Isolate Medial Sounds		8 / 10	___ / 10		
Identify Phonemes		8 / 10	___ / 10		
Categorize Phonemes		8 / 10	___ / 10		
Blend Phonemes		8 / 10	___ / 10		
Segment Phonemes		8 / 10	___ / 10		
Delete Phonemes		8 / 10	___ / 10		
Add Phonemes		8 / 10	___ / 10		
Substitute Phonemes		8 / 10	___ / 10		
Inventory Total		148 / 185	___ / 185		

Kindergarten • Summary Recording Form

Name _____ Teacher _____ School year _____

Progress-Monitoring Assessments (PMA)	Date Given	Segment Phonemes	Letter Naming	Letter-Sound Relationships	High-Frequency Words	Reading Sentences	Actions (Check One)	
							Move Ahead	Needs Reteaching
PMA Form 1 Sessions K.56, K.57, K.58, K.59, K.60, K.61, K.62		Goal 3 / 3 ____ / 3	Goal 15 / 18 ____ / 18	Goal 3 / 3 ____ / 3		Goal 4 / 4 ____ / 4		
PMA Form 2 Sessions K.63, K.64, K.65, K.66, K.67		Goal 3 / 3 ____ / 3	Goal 8 / 11 ____ / 11	Goal 3 / 3 ____ / 3	Goal 4 / 4 ____ / 4	Goal 5 / 6 ____ / 6		

Progress-Monitoring Assessments (PMA)	Date Given	Segment Phonemes	Letter-Sound Relationships	High-Frequency Words	Decoding Words	Reading Sentences	Actions (Check One)	
							Move Ahead	Needs Reteaching
PMA Form 3 Sessions K.68, K.69, K.70, K.71, K.72		Goal 3 / 3 ____ / 3	Goal 3 / 3 ____ / 3	Goal 7 / 8 ____ / 8		Goal 5 / 6 ____ / 6		
PMA Form 4 Sessions K.73A, K.73B		Goal 3 / 3 ____ / 3	Goal 3 / 3 ____ / 3	Goal 5 / 6 ____ / 6	Goal 7 / 8 ____ / 8	Goal 8 / 9 ____ / 9		
PMA Form 5 Sessions K.74A, K.74B, K.75A, K.75B		Goal 3 / 3 ____ / 3	Goal 3 / 3 ____ / 3	Goal 7 / 8 ____ / 8	Goal 8 / 10 ____ / 10	Goal 9 / 11 ____ / 11		
PMA Form 6 Sessions K.76A, K.76B, K.77		Goal 3 / 3 ____ / 3	Goal 3 / 3 ____ / 3	Goal 7 / 8 ____ / 8	Goal 8 / 10 ____ / 10	Goal 10 / 12 ____ / 12		
PMA Form 7 Sessions K.78A, K.78B, K.79A, K.79B		Goal 3 / 3 ____ / 3	Goal 3 / 3 ____ / 3	Goal 7 / 8 ____ / 8	Goal 8 / 10 ____ / 10	Goal 13 / 15 ____ / 15		

Kindergarten • Summary Recording Form

Progress-Monitoring Assessments (PMA)	Date Given	Segment Phonemes	Letter-Sound Relationships	High-Frequency Words	Decoding Words	Reading Sentences	Actions (Check One)	
							Move Ahead	Needs Reteaching
PMA Form 8 Sessions K.80A, K.80B, K.81A, K.81B		Goal 3 / 3 ____ / 3	Goal 3 / 3 ____ / 3	Goal 7 / 8 ____ / 8	Goal 8 / 10 ____ / 10	Goal 11 / 13 ____ / 13		
PMA Form 9 Sessions K.82, K.83A, K.83B		Goal 3 / 3 ____ / 3	Goal 3 / 3 ____ / 3	Goal 7 / 8 ____ / 8	Goal 8 / 10 ____ / 10	Goal 13 / 15 ____ / 15		
PMA Form 10 Sessions K.84A, K.84B, K.85A, K.85B		Goal 3 / 3 ____ / 3	Goal 3 / 3 ____ / 3	Goal 7 / 8 ____ / 8	Goal 8 / 10 ____ / 10	Goal 19 / 21 ____ / 21		
PMA Form 11 Sessions K.86A, K.86B, K.87		Goal 3 / 3 ____ / 3	Goal 3 / 3 ____ / 3	Goal 7 / 8 ____ / 8	Goal 8 / 10 ____ / 10	Goal 18 / 20 ____ / 20		
PMA Form 12 Sessions K.88A, K.88B, K.89A, K.89B		Goal 3 / 3 ____ / 3	Goal 3 / 3 ____ / 3	Goal 7 / 8 ____ / 8	Goal 8 / 10 ____ / 10	Goal 18 / 20 ____ / 20		
PMA Form 13 Sessions K.90A, K.90B, K.91A, K.91B		Goal 3 / 3 ____ / 3	Goal 3 / 3 ____ / 3	Goal 7 / 8 ____ / 8	Goal 8 / 10 ____ / 10	Goal 20 / 22 ____ / 22		
PMA Form 14 Sessions K.92, K.93A, K.93B		Goal 3 / 3 ____ / 3	Goal 3 / 3 ____ / 3	Goal 7 / 8 ____ / 8	Goal 8 / 10 ____ / 10	Goal 21 / 23 ____ / 23		
PMA Form 15 Sessions K.94A, K.94B, K.94C, K.95		Goal 3 / 3 ____ / 3	Goal 3 / 3 ____ / 3	Goal 7 / 8 ____ / 8	Goal 8 / 10 ____ / 10	Goal 20 / 22 ____ / 22		

Notes:

Grade 1 • Summary Recording Form

Name _____ Teacher _____ School year _____

Screening Assessments	Date Given	Score		Actions (Check One)	
		Goal	Student's Score	Meets Goals	Needs Intervention
Letter-Naming Fluency Lowercase — Beginning-of-Year		18 out of 26 letters	____ /26		
Letter-Naming Fluency Lowercase — Mid-Year		24 out of 26 letters	____ /26		
Letter-Naming Fluency Uppercase — Beginning-of-Year		18 out of 26 letters	____ /26		
Letter-Naming Fluency Uppercase — Mid-Year		24 out of 26 letters	____ /26		
Phoneme Segmentation — Beginning-of-Year		6 / 10	____ /10		
Phoneme Segmentation — Mid-Year		8 / 10	____ /10		
Nonsense-Word Reading CVC Pattern Words — Beginning-of-Year		6 / 10	____ /10		
Nonsense-Word Reading CVC Pattern Words — Mid-Year		8 / 10	____ /10		
Nonsense-Word Reading CVCe Pattern Words — Beginning-of-Year		6 / 10	____ /10		
Nonsense-Word Reading CVCe Pattern Words — Mid-Year		8 / 10	____ /10		
Nonsense-Word Reading Other Words — Beginning-of-Year		6 / 10	____ /10		
Nonsense-Word Reading Other Words — Mid-Year		8 / 10	____ /10		
Word Identification High-Frequency Words — Beginning-of-Year		6 / 10	____ /10		
Word Identification High-Frequency Words — Mid-Year		8 / 10	____ /10		
Word Identification Multisyllabic Words — Beginning-of-Year		6 / 10	____ /10		
Word Identification Multisyllabic Words — Mid-Year		8 / 10	____ /10		
Oral Reading Fluency — Mid-Year		13–33 WCPM	____ / WCPM		

Intervention Assessments
Copyright © Houghton Mifflin Harcourt Publishing Company.

Grade 1

Grade 1 • Summary Recording Form

Name _____ Teacher _____ School year _____

Progress-Monitoring Assessments (PMA)	Date Given	Decoding Words	High-Frequency Words	Reading Sentences	Actions (Check One)	
					Move Ahead	Needs Reteaching
PMA Form 1 Sessions 1.1A-C, 1.2A-B		Goal 8 / 10 ___/ 10	Goal 5 / 6 ___/ 6	Goal 13 / 15 ___/ 15		
PMA Form 2 Sessions 1.3A-D, 1.4A-D		Goal 8 / 10 ___/ 10	Goal 8 / 10 ___/ 10	Goal 14 / 16 ___/ 16		
PMA Form 3 Sessions 1.5A-C, 1.6A-C		Goal 8 / 10 ___/ 10	Goal 8 / 10 ___/ 10	Goal 12 / 14 ___/ 14		
PMA Form 4 Sessions 1.7, 1.8A-D		Goal 8 / 10 ___/ 10	Goal 8 / 10 ___/ 10	Goal 16 / 18 ___/ 18		
PMA Form 5 Sessions 1.9A-C, 1.10A-C		Goal 8 / 10 ___/ 10	Goal 8 / 10 ___/ 10	Goal 18 / 21 ___/ 21		
PMA Form 6 Sessions 1.11A-B, 1.12A-C		Goal 8 / 10 ___/ 10	Goal 8 / 10 ___/ 10	Goal 17 / 19 ___/ 19		
PMA Form 7 Sessions 1.13, 1.14A-C		Goal 8 / 10 ___/ 10	Goal 8 / 10 ___/ 10	Goal 22 / 25 ___/ 25		
PMA Form 8 Sessions 1.15A-D, 1.16A-D		Goal 8 / 10 ___/ 10	Goal 8 / 10 ___/ 10	Goal 26 / 30 ___/ 30		
PMA Form 9 Sessions 1.17A-D, 1.18A-D		Goal 8 / 10 ___/ 10	Goal 8 / 10 ___/ 10	Goal 31 / 34 ___/ 34		
PMA Form 10 Sessions 1.19, 1.20A-D		Goal 8 / 10 ___/ 10	Goal 8 / 10 ___/ 10	Goal 38 / 44 ___/ 44		

Grade 1 • Summary Recording Form

Progress-Monitoring Assessments (PMA)	Date Given	Decoding Words	High-Frequency Words	Oral Reading Fluency Enter Words Correct per Minute (WCPM)	Retelling (Goal 2 / 2)	Actions (Check One)	
						Move Ahead	Needs Reteaching
PMA Form 11 Sessions 1.21A–D, 1.22A-D		Goal 8 / 10 ___ / 10	Goal 8 / 10 ___ / 10	Goal 13–33 WCPM ___ / WCPM	___ /2		
PMA Form 12 Sessions 1.23A-C, 1.24A-D		Goal 8 / 10 ___ / 10	Goal 8 / 10 ___ / 10	Goal 13–33 WCPM ___ / WCPM	___ /2		
PMA Form 13 Sessions 1.25, 1.26A-D		Goal 8 / 10 ___ / 10	Goal 8 / 10 ___ / 10	Goal 13–33 WCPM ___ / WCPM	___ /2		
PMA Form 14 Sessions 1.27A-C, 1.28A-C		Goal 8 / 10 ___ / 10	Goal 8 / 10 ___ / 10	Goal 13–33 WCPM ___ / WCPM	___ /2		
PMA Form 15 Sessions 1.29A-B, 1.30A-B		Goal 8 / 10 ___ / 10	Goal 8 / 10 ___ / 10	Goal 13–33 WCPM ___ / WCPM	___ /2		
PMA Form 16 Sessions 1.31, 1.32A-D		Goal 8 / 10 ___ / 10	Goal 8 / 10 ___ / 10	Goal 43–63 WCPM ___ / WCPM	___ /2		
PMA Form 17 Sessions 1.33A-D, 1.34A-D		Goal 8 / 10 ___ / 10	Goal 8 / 10 ___ / 10	Goal 43–63 WCPM ___ / WCPM	___ /2		
PMA Form 18 Sessions 1.35A-C, 1.36A-C, 1.37		Goal 8 / 10 ___ / 10	Goal 8 / 10 ___ / 10	Goal 43–63 WCPM ___ / WCPM	___ /2		

Notes: _____

Grade 2 • Summary Recording Form

Name _____ Teacher _____ School year _____

Screening Assessments	Date Given	Score		Actions (Check One)	
		Goal	Student's Score	Meets Goals	Needs Intervention
Word Identification High-Frequency Words		8 / 10	____ / 10		
Word Identification Multisyllabic Words		8 / 10	____ / 10		
Oral Reading Fluency		Fluency 41–61 WCPM	____ / WCPM		
		Comprehension (Goal 2 / 2)	____ / 2		

Progress-Monitoring Assessments (PMA)	Date Given	Score Enter Words Correct per Minute (WCPM)		Comprehension (Goal 2 / 2)	Actions (Check One)	
		Goal	Student's Score		Move Ahead	Needs Reteaching
PMA Form 1 Sessions 2.1A–B, 2.2A–B		41–61 WCPM	____ / WCPM	____ / 2		
PMA Form 2 Sessions 2.3A–C, 2.4A–C		41–61 WCPM	____ / WCPM	____ / 2		
PMA Form 3 Sessions 2.5A–B, 2.6		41–61 WCPM	____ / WCPM	____ / 2		
PMA Form 4 Sessions 2.7A–B, 2.8A–C		41–61 WCPM	____ / WCPM	____ / 2		

Grade 2 • Summary Recording Form

Name _____ Teacher _____ School year _____

Progress-Monitoring Assessments (PMA)	Date Given	Score Enter Words Correct per Minute (WCPM)		Comprehension (Goal 2 / 2)	Actions (Check One)	
		Goal	Student's Score		Move Ahead	Needs Reteaching
PMA Form 5 Sessions 2.9A-C, 2.10A-C		41–61 WCPM	____ / WCPM	____ / 2		
PMA Form 6 Sessions 2.11A-B, 2.12		41–61 WCPM	____ / WCPM	____ / 2		
PMA Form 7 Sessions 2.13A-B, 2.14A-B		62–82 WCPM	____ / WCPM	____ / 2		
PMA Form 8 Sessions 2.15A-B, 2.16A-B		62–82 WCPM	____ / WCPM	____ / 2		
PMA Form 9 Sessions 2.17A-C, 2.18		62–82 WCPM	____ / WCPM	____ / 2		
PMA Form 10 Sessions 2.19A-B, 2.20A-B		62–82 WCPM	____ / WCPM	____ / 2		
PMA Form 11 Sessions 2.21A-C, 2.22A-B		62–82 WCPM	____ / WCPM	____ / 2		
PMA Form 12 Sessions 2.23A-B, 2.24		62–82 WCPM	____ / WCPM	____ / 2		
PMA Form 13 Sessions 2.25A-C, 2.26A-C		62–82 WCPM	____ / WCPM	____ / 2		
PMA Form 14 Sessions 2.27A-C, 2.28A-C		79–99 WCPM	____ / WCPM	____ / 2		
PMA Form 15 Sessions 2.29A-B, 2.30		79–99 WCPM	____ / WCPM	____ / 2		
PMA Form 16 Sessions 2.31A-B, 2.32A-C		79–99 WCPM	____ / WCPM	____ / 2		

Grade 2 • Summary Recording Form

Name _____ Teacher _____ School year _____

Progress-Monitoring Assessments (PMA)	Date Given	Score — Enter Words Correct per Minute (WCPM)		Comprehension (Goal 2 / 2)	Actions (Check One)	
		Goal	Student's Score		Move Ahead	Needs Reteaching
PMA Form 17 Sessions 2.33A–B, 2.34A–C		79–99 WCPM	____ / WCPM	____ / 2		
PMA Form 18 Sessions 2.35A–C, 2.36		79–99 WCPM	____ / WCPM	____ / 2		

Notes:

_____

_____

_____

_____

_____

_____

_____

_____

Grade 3 • Summary Recording Form

Name _____ Teacher _____ School year _____

Screening Assessments	Date Given	Score — Enter Words Correct per Minute (WCPM)		Comprehension (Goal 2 / 2)	Actions (Check One)	
		Goal	Student's Score		Move Ahead	Needs Reteaching
Oral Reading Fluency		61–81 WCPM	____ / WCPM	____ / 2		

Progress-Monitoring Assessments (PMA)	Date Given	Score — Enter Words Correct per Minute (WCPM)		Comprehension (Goal 2 / 2)	Actions (Check One)	
		Goal	Student's Score		Move Ahead	Needs Reteaching
PMA Form 1 Sessions 3.1, 3.2A–B		61–81 WCPM	____ / WCPM	____ / 2		
PMA Form 2 Sessions 3.3, 3.4		61–81 WCPM	____ / WCPM	____ / 2		
PMA Form 3 Sessions 3.5, 3.6		61–81 WCPM	____ / WCPM	____ / 2		
PMA Form 4 Sessions 3.7, 3.8		61–81 WCPM	____ / WCPM	____ / 2		
PMA Form 5 Sessions 3.9, 3.10		61–81 WCPM	____ / WCPM	____ / 2		
PMA Form 6 Sessions 3.11, 3.12		61–81 WCPM	____ / WCPM	____ / 2		
PMA Form 7 Sessions 3.13, 3.14		82–102 WCPM	____ / WCPM	____ / 2		
PMA Form 8 Sessions 3.15, 3.16		82–102 WCPM	____ / WCPM	____ / 2		

Grade 3 • Summary Recording Form

Name _____ Teacher _____ School year _____

Progress-Monitoring Assessments (PMA)	Date Given	Score Enter Words Correct per Minute (WCPM)		Comprehension (Goal 2 / 2)	Actions (Check One)	
		Goal	Student's Score		Move Ahead	Needs Reteaching
PMA Form 9 Sessions 3.17, 3.18		82–102 WCPM	___ / WCPM	___ /2		
PMA Form 10 Sessions 3.19, 3.20		82–102 WCPM	___ / WCPM	___ /2		
PMA Form 11 Sessions 3.21, 3.22		82–102 WCPM	___ / WCPM	___ /2		
PMA Form 12 Sessions 3.23, 3.24		82–102 WCPM	___ / WCPM	___ /2		
PMA Form 13 Sessions 3.25, 3.26		82–102 WCPM	___ / WCPM	___ /2		
PMA Form 14 Sessions 3.27, 3.28A–B		97–117 WCPM	___ / WCPM	___ /2		
PMA Form 15 Sessions 3.29, 3.30		97–117 WCPM	___ / WCPM	___ /2		
PMA Form 16 Sessions 3.31, 3.32		97–117 WCPM	___ / WCPM	___ /2		
PMA Form 17 Sessions 3.33, 3.34		97–117 WCPM	___ / WCPM	___ /2		
PMA Form 18 Sessions 3.35, 3.36		97–117 WCPM	___ / WCPM	___ /2		

Notes:

Grade 4 • Summary Recording Form

Name _____ Teacher _____ School year _____

Screening Assessments	Date Given	Score Enter Words Correct per Minute (WCPM)		Comprehension (Goal 2 / 2)	Actions (Check One)	
		Goal	Student's Score		Move Ahead	Needs Reteaching
Oral Reading Fluency		84–104 WCPM	____ / WCPM	____ / 2		

Progress-Monitoring Assessments (PMA)	Date Given	Score Enter Words Correct per Minute (WCPM)		Comprehension (Goal 2 / 2)	Actions (Check One)	
		Goal	Student's Score		Move Ahead	Needs Reteaching
PMA Form 1 Sessions 4-6.1, 4-6.2		84–104 WCPM	____ / WCPM	____ / 2		
PMA Form 2 Sessions 4-6.3, 4-6.4		84–104 WCPM	____ / WCPM	____ / 2		
PMA Form 3 Sessions 4-6.5, 4-6.6		84–104 WCPM	____ / WCPM	____ / 2		
PMA Form 4 Sessions 4-6.7, 4-6.8		84–104 WCPM	____ / WCPM	____ / 2		
PMA Form 5 Sessions 4-6.9, 4-6.10		84–104 WCPM	____ / WCPM	____ / 2		
PMA Form 6 Sessions 4-6.11, 4-6.12		84–104 WCPM	____ / WCPM	____ / 2		
PMA Form 7 Sessions 4-6.13, 4-6.14		84–104 WCPM	____ / WCPM	____ / 2		
PMA Form 8 Sessions 4-6.15, 4-6.16		102–122 WCPM	____ / WCPM	____ / 2		

Grade 4 • Summary Recording Form

Name _____ Teacher _____ School year _____

Progress-Monitoring Assessments (PMA)	Date Given	Score — Enter Words Correct per Minute (WCPM)		Comprehension (Goal 2 / 2)	Actions (Check One)	
		Goal	Student's Score		Move Ahead	Needs Reteaching
PMA Form 9 Sessions 4-6.17, 4-6.18		102–122 WCPM	___ / WCPM	___ /2		
PMA Form 10 Sessions 4-6.19, 4-6.20		102–122 WCPM	___ / WCPM	___ /2		
PMA Form 11 Sessions 4-6.21, 4-6.22		102–122 WCPM	___ / WCPM	___ /2		
PMA Form 12 Sessions 4-6.23, 4-6.24		102–122 WCPM	___ / WCPM	___ /2		
PMA Form 13 Sessions 4-6.25, 4-6.26		102–122 WCPM	___ / WCPM	___ /2		
PMA Form 14 Sessions 4-6.27, 4-6.28		102–122 WCPM	___ / WCPM	___ /2		
PMA Form 15 Sessions 4-6.29, 4-6.30		102–122 WCPM	___ / WCPM	___ /2		
PMA Form 16 Sessions 4-6.31, 4-6.32		113–133 WCPM	___ / WCPM	___ /2		
PMA Form 17 Sessions 4-6.33, 4-6.34		113–133 WCPM	___ / WCPM	___ /2		
PMA Form 18 Sessions 4-6.35, 4-6.36		113–133 WCPM	___ / WCPM	___ /2		
PMA Form 19 Sessions 4-6.37, 4-6.38		113–133 WCPM	___ / WCPM	___ /2		

Grade 4 • Summary Recording Form

Name _____ Teacher _____ School year _____

Progress-Monitoring Assessments (PMA)	Date Given	Score — Enter Words Correct per Minute (WCPM)		Comprehension (Goal 2 / 2)	Actions (Check One)	
		Goal	Student's Score		Move Ahead	Needs Reteaching
PMA Form 20 Sessions 4-6.39, 4-6.40		113–133 WCPM	_____ / WCPM	_____ / 2		
PMA Form 21 Sessions 4-6.41, 4-6.42		113–133 WCPM	_____ / WCPM	_____ / 2		

Notes: _____

_____

_____

_____

_____

_____

_____

_____

_____

_____

_____

Grade 5 • Summary Recording Form

Name _____ Teacher _____ School year _____

Screening Assessments	Date Given	Score		Comprehension (Goal 2 / 2)	Actions (Check One)	
		Enter Words Correct per Minute (WCPM)			Move Ahead	Needs Reteaching
		Goal	Student's Score			
Oral Reading Fluency		100–120 WCPM	_____ / WCPM	_____ / 2		

Progress-Monitoring Assessments (PMA)	Date Given	Score		Comprehension (Goal 2 / 2)	Actions (Check One)	
		Enter Words Correct per Minute (WCPM)			Move Ahead	Needs Reteaching
		Goal	Student's Score			
PMA Form 1 Sessions 4-6.1, 4-6.2		100–120 WCPM	_____ / WCPM	_____ / 2		
PMA Form 2 Sessions 4-6.3, 4-6.4		100–120 WCPM	_____ / WCPM	_____ / 2		
PMA Form 3 Sessions 4-6.5, 4-6.6		100–120 WCPM	_____ / WCPM	_____ / 2		
PMA Form 4 Sessions 4-6.7, 4-6.8		100–120 WCPM	_____ / WCPM	_____ / 2		
PMA Form 5 Sessions 4-6.9, 4-6.10		100–120 WCPM	_____ / WCPM	_____ / 2		
PMA Form 6 Sessions 4-6.11, 4-6.12		100–120 WCPM	_____ / WCPM	_____ / 2		
PMA Form 7 Sessions 4-6.13, 4-6.14		100–120 WCPM	_____ / WCPM	_____ / 2		
PMA Form 8 Sessions 4-6.15, 4-6.16		117–137 WCPM	_____ / WCPM	_____ / 2		

Grade 5 • Summary Recording Form

Name _____ Teacher _____ School year _____

Progress-Monitoring Assessments (PMA)	Date Given	Score Enter Words Correct per Minute (WCPM)		Comprehension (Goal 2 / 2)	Actions (Check One)	
		Goal	Student's Score		Move Ahead	Needs Reteaching
PMA Form 9 Sessions 4-6.17, 4-6.18		117–137 WCPM	____ / WCPM	____ / 2		
PMA Form 10 Sessions 4-6.19, 4-6.20		117–137 WCPM	____ / WCPM	____ / 2		
PMA Form 11 Sessions 4-6.21, 4-6.22		117–137 WCPM	____ / WCPM	____ / 2		
PMA Form 12 Sessions 4-6.23, 4-6.24		117–137 WCPM	____ / WCPM	____ / 2		
PMA Form 13 Sessions 4-6.25, 4-6.26		117–137 WCPM	____ / WCPM	____ / 2		
PMA Form 14 Sessions 4-6.27, 4-6.28		117–137 WCPM	____ / WCPM	____ / 2		
PMA Form 15 Sessions 4-6.29, 4-6.30		117–137 WCPM	____ / WCPM	____ / 2		
PMA Form 16 Sessions 4-6.31, 4-6.32		129–149 WCPM	____ / WCPM	____ / 2		
PMA Form 17 Sessions 4-6.33, 4-6.34		129–149 WCPM	____ / WCPM	____ / 2		
PMA Form 18 Sessions 4-6.35, 4-6.36		129–149 WCPM	____ / WCPM	____ / 2		
PMA Form 19 Sessions 4-6.37, 4-6.38		129–149 WCPM	____ / WCPM	____ / 2		

Grade 5 • Summary Recording Form

Name _____ Teacher _____ School year _____

Progress-Monitoring Assessments (PMA)	Date Given	Score Enter Words Correct per Minute (WCPM)		Comprehension (Goal 2 / 2)	Actions (Check One)	
		Goal	Student's Score		Move Ahead	Needs Reteaching
PMA Form 20 Sessions 4-6.39, 4-6.40		129–149 WCPM	_____ / WCPM	_____ / 2		
PMA Form 21 Sessions 4-6.41, 4-6.42		129–149 WCPM	_____ / WCPM	_____ / 2		

Notes: _____

_____

_____

_____

_____

_____

_____

_____

_____

Grade 6 • Summary Recording Form

Name _____ Teacher _____ School year _____

Screening Assessments	Date Given	Score — Enter Words Correct per Minute (WCPM)		Comprehension (Goal 2 / 2)	Actions (Check One)	
		Goal	Student's Score		Move Ahead	Needs Reteaching
Oral Reading Fluency		117–137 WCPM	_____ / WCPM	_____ / 2		

Progress-Monitoring Assessments (PMA)	Date Given	Score — Enter Words Correct per Minute (WCPM)		Comprehension (Goal 2 / 2)	Actions (Check One)	
		Goal	Student's Score		Move Ahead	Needs Reteaching
PMA Form 1 Sessions 4-6.1, 4-6.2		117–137 WCPM	_____ / WCPM	_____ / 2		
PMA Form 2 Sessions 4-6.3, 4-6.4		117–137 WCPM	_____ / WCPM	_____ / 2		
PMA Form 3 Sessions 4-6.5, 4-6.6		117–137 WCPM	_____ / WCPM	_____ / 2		
PMA Form 4 Sessions 4-6.7, 4-6.8		117–137 WCPM	_____ / WCPM	_____ / 2		
PMA Form 5 Sessions 4-6.9, 4-6.10		117–137 WCPM	_____ / WCPM	_____ / 2		
PMA Form 6 Sessions 4-6.11, 4-6.12		117–137 WCPM	_____ / WCPM	_____ / 2		
PMA Form 7 Sessions 4-6.13, 4-6.14		117–137 WCPM	_____ / WCPM	_____ / 2		
PMA Form 8 Sessions 4-6.15, 4-6.16		130–150 WCPM	_____ / WCPM	_____ / 2		

Grade 6 • Summary Recording Form

Progress-Monitoring Assessments (PMA)	Date Given	Score — Enter Words Correct per Minute (WCPM)		Comprehension (Goal 2 / 2)	Actions (Check One)	
		Goal	Student's Score		Move Ahead	Needs Reteaching
PMA Form 9 Sessions 4-6.17, 4-6.18		130–150 WCPM	____ / WCPM	____ / 2		
PMA Form 10 Sessions 4-6.19, 4-6.20		130–150 WCPM	____ / WCPM	____ / 2		
PMA Form 11 Sessions 4-6.21, 4-6.22		130–150 WCPM	____ / WCPM	____ / 2		
PMA Form 12 Sessions 4-6.23, 4-6.24		130–150 WCPM	____ / WCPM	____ / 2		
PMA Form 13 Sessions 4-6.25, 4-6.26		130–150 WCPM	____ / WCPM	____ / 2		
PMA Form 14 Sessions 4-6.27, 4-6.28		130–150 WCPM	____ / WCPM	____ / 2		
PMA Form 15 Sessions 4-6.29, 4-6.30		130–150 WCPM	____ / WCPM	____ / 2		
PMA Form 16 Sessions 4-6.31, 4-6.32		140–160 WCPM	____ / WCPM	____ / 2		
PMA Form 17 Sessions 4-6.33, 4-6.34		140–160 WCPM	____ / WCPM	____ / 2		
PMA Form 18 Sessions 4-6.35, 4-6.36		140–160 WCPM	____ / WCPM	____ / 2		
PMA Form 19 Sessions 4-6.37, 4-6.38		140–160 WCPM	____ / WCPM	____ / 2		

Grade 6 • Summary Recording Form

Name _____ Teacher _____ School year _____

Progress-Monitoring Assessments (PMA)	Date Given	Score Enter Words Correct per Minute (WCPM)		Comprehension (Goal 2 / 2)	Actions (Check One)	
		Goal	Student's Score		Move Ahead	Needs Reteaching
PMA Form 20 Sessions 4-6.39, 4-6.40		140–160 WCPM	___ / WCPM	___ / 2		
PMA Form 21 Sessions 4-6.41, 4-6.42		140–160 WCPM	___ / WCPM	___ / 2		

Notes: _____

_____

_____

_____

_____

_____

_____

_____

_____

_____

Screening Assessments

T   D   I   L

N   W   G   Z

J   A   M   U

C   H   B   K

E   O   R   V

X   P   S   Y

Q   F

d   y   w   l

p   r   j   x

e   m   t   o

s   f   k   b

q   h   u   i

g   v   z   n

a   c

Name _____ Date _____

Letter-Naming Identification

T	_____	d	_____
D	_____	y	_____
I	_____	w	_____
L	_____	l	_____
N	_____	p	_____
W	_____	r	_____
G	_____	j	_____
Z	_____	x	_____
J	_____	e	_____
A	_____	m	_____
M	_____	t	_____
U	_____	o	_____
C	_____	s	_____
H	_____	f	_____
B	_____	k	_____
K	_____	b	_____
E	_____	q	_____
O	_____	h	_____
R	_____	u	_____
V	_____	i	_____
X	_____	g	_____
P	_____	v	_____
S	_____	z	_____
Y	_____	n	_____
Q	_____	a	_____
F	_____	c	_____

Name _____ Date _____

Task: The child will listen to a word and produce each phoneme in the word separately.

Model: **Say:** *I am going to say a word. Then I am going to say each sound. Listen carefully for each sound. The word is* **sat***. The sounds in* **sat** *are /s/-/ă/-/t/. Be sure to articulate each sound separately. Do not simply stretch out the word.*

Sample: **Then say:** *Listen to this word. This time you tell me the sounds in the word. Listen carefully:* **bite***. What sounds do you hear in* **bite***?* Pause and wait for the child to respond. *(/b/-/ī/-/t/) You're correct. The sounds in the word* **bite** *are /b/-/ī/-/t/.*

          Then say: *Now listen to some more words. Tell me the sounds you hear in these words.* Provide no additional help with the items below. Record the child's response.

What sounds are in _____ ?	
1. man (/m/ /ă/ /n/)	
2. sip (/s/ /ĭ/ /p/	
3. leg (/l/ /ĕ/ /g/)	
4. not (/n/ /ŏ/ /t/)	
5. tub (/t/ /ŭ/ /b/)	
6. joke (/j/ /ō/ /k/)	
7. hide (/h/ /ī/ /d/)	
8. face (/f/ /ā/ /s/)	
9. rude (/r/ /ū/ /d/)	
10. beep (/b/ /ē/ /p/)	

Score: _____ /10

zal	nug
keb	vop
dit	jis
maf	ruv
weg	hox

rame	wope
bine	hute
zete	sabe
fode	lipe
jime	noke

breet

plog

leck

wuff

zaw

strime

thode

vant

shabe

netch

Name _____ Date _____

Nonsense-Word Reading

CVC Words

zal _____   nug _____

keb _____   vop _____

dit _____   jis _____

maf _____   ruv _____

weg _____   hox _____

Goal 8/10 Score _____ / 10

CVCe Words

rame _____   wope _____

bine _____   hute _____

zete _____   sabe _____

fode _____   lipe _____

jime _____   noke _____

Goal 8/10 Score _____ / 10

Other Words

breet _____   plog _____

leck _____   wuff _____

zaw _____   strime _____

thode _____   vant _____

shabe _____   netch _____

Goal 8/10 Score _____ / 10

are

would

some

find

have

write

help

like

pull

she

little

wishes

funny

today

ruler

asking

animal

many

reading

pictures

Name _____ Date _____

Word Identification

High-Frequency Words

are _____

some _____

have _____

help _____

pull _____

would _____

find _____

write _____

like _____

she _____

Goal 8/10   Score _____ / 10

Multisyllabic Words

little _____

funny _____

ruler _____

animal _____

reading _____

wishes _____

today _____

asking _____

many _____

pictures _____

Goal 8/10   Score _____ / 10

Max and His Pets

Pal is a dog. Pal is brown and yellow. Max likes Pal. Pal is big. Pal is fun. Max likes to play with Pal. Max and Pal play tag. Pal likes to run. He likes to get wet.

Puff is a cat. Puff is little. Puff has white fur. Puff likes to purr and nap. Pal likes to play with Puff. Pal likes to chase Puff's tail. Puff runs to Max for help.

Puff and Pal like this box. Puff and Pal play in it. The box is not big. Can Max fit in the box?

Max hid the box. Pal and Puff try to find the box. Pal barks loudly. Puff scratches the door.

What will Pal and Puff do now? What will the pets play with?

Max and His Pets   4

Pal is a dog. Pal is brown and yellow. Max   14

likes Pal. Pal is big. Pal is fun. Max likes to play   26

with Pal. Max and Pal play tag. Pal likes to run. He   38

likes to get wet.   42

Puff is a cat. Puff is little. Puff has white fur.   53

Puff likes to purr and nap. Pal likes to play with   64

Puff. Pal likes to chase Puff's tail. Puff runs to Max 75

for help.   77

Puff and Pal like this box. Puff and Pal play in   88

it. The box is not big. Can Max fit in the box?   100

Max hid the box. Pal and Puff try to find the   111

box. Pal barks loudly. Puff scratches the door.   119

What will Pal and Puff do now? What will the   129

pets play with?   132

_____ / WCPM

mind	comes
sleep	right
walked	cried
before	know
other	against

family

places

myself

wouldn't

table

started

another

thinking

really

catches

Name _____ Date _____

Word Identification

High-Frequency Words	Multisyllabic Words
mind _____	family _____
sleep _____	places _____
walked _____	myself _____
before _____	wouldn't _____
other _____	table _____
comes _____	started _____
right _____	another _____
cried _____	thinking _____
know _____	really _____
against _____	catches _____

Goal 8/10   Score _____ / 10   Goal 8/10   Score _____ / 10

Fox

A fox looks like a small, thin dog. Its face looks like a dog's face. Its teeth look like a dog's teeth. It has long legs, just like a dog.

The fox knows how to hunt. This animal can see and hear quite well. The fox has a good sense of smell, too. It hunts mice and rats, as well as birds and frogs. A fox will eat just about anything it can catch.

This fox is a red fox. It hunts like a cat. Like a cat, the red fox can see well at night. If the fox spots a mouse, it stops and stays very still. Then it pounces, like a cat.

This fox is a gray fox. Its coat is black and white. Its tail has a black tip. This fox is also called a tree fox. It can climb trees, like a cat!

The fox looks like a dog in most ways. But sometimes, it acts like a cat!

Fox

1

A fox looks like a small, thin dog. Its face   11

looks like a dog's face. Its teeth look like a dog's   22

teeth. It has long legs, just like a dog.   31

The fox knows how to hunt. This animal can   40

see and hear quite well. The fox has a good sense   51

of smell, too. It hunts mice and rats, as well as   62

birds and frogs. A fox will eat just about anything   72

it can catch.   75

This fox is a red fox. It hunts like a cat. Like   87

a cat, the red fox can see well at night. If the fox   100

spots a mouse, it stops and stays very still. Then it   111

pounces, like a cat.   115

This fox is a gray fox. Its coat is black and   126

white. Its tail has a black tip. This fox is also called   138

a tree fox. It can climb trees, like a cat!   148

The fox looks like a dog in most ways. But   158

sometimes, it acts like a cat!   164

_____ / WCPM

Feeding Birds

When you look outside, do you see birds? They may be looking for food. Different kinds of birds look for food in different places. That is why there are many types of bird feeders.

Hummingbirds and orioles eat from hummingbird feeders. This kind of feeder holds sugar water. The birds sip the water through a tube. Most hummingbird feeders hang from a hook.

Another kind of feeder is a post feeder. It holds seeds. The feeder sits on top of a tall post. Many birds like to perch on the feeder. That way they can stay in one place and eat. Robins, woodpeckers, and doves eat at a post feeder.

A third kind of feeder is a thistle tube feeder. Thistle seeds are very fine and thin. The feeder is long and skinny. It has thin slits in the side. This lets small birds get food and keeps large birds out. Finches like these feeders!

Many birds eat from the ground. You can feed them from a tray feeder. A tray feeder is flat like a plate. Sparrows, wrens, and blue jays like to eat from tray feeders.

Feeding Birds

When you look outside, do you see birds? They	11

When you look outside, do you see birds? They 2

may be looking for food. Different kinds of birds look 21

for food in different places. That is why there are many 32

types of bird feeders. 36

Hummingbirds and orioles eat from hummingbird 42

feeders. This kind of feeder holds sugar water. The 51

birds sip the water through a tube. Most hummingbird 60

feeders hang from a hook. 65

Another kind of feeder is a post feeder. It holds 75

seeds. The feeder sits on top of a tall post. Many birds 87

like to perch on the feeder. That way they can stay in 99

one place and eat. Robins, woodpeckers, and doves 107

eat at a post feeder. 112

A third kind of feeder is a thistle tube feeder. 122

Thistle seeds are very fine and thin. The feeder is long 133

and skinny. It has thin slits in the side. This lets small 145

birds get food and keeps large birds out. Finches like 155

these feeders! 157

Many birds eat from the ground. You can feed 166

them from a tray feeder. A tray feeder is flat like a 178

plate. Sparrows, wrens, and blue jays like to eat from 188

tray feeders. 190

_____ / WCPM

Komodo Dragons

Dragons are scary monsters in stories, legends, and movies. But have you ever wondered whether they were real?

Imagine heading out for a day of fishing. You see an island that looks like a good fishing spot. As you approach the island, you see creatures bigger than your small fishing boat that look like dragons.

In 1912, a group of fishermen who went to Komodo Island had a frightening experience just like the one described. They spotted huge creatures that looked like dragons. The fishermen told their dragon stories when they returned home, but the stories did not get a lot of attention.

In 1926, the American Museum of Natural History sponsored a trip to Komodo. The expedition confirmed that the fishermen's stories were true. They studied the creatures and called them Komodo dragons.

A Komodo dragon is the largest living lizard. Grown Komodo dragons are between seven and nine feet long and weigh between 150 and 300 pounds.

Komodo dragons eat meat. They hunt small deer and wild pigs by hiding in the grass and waiting. Then they lean out and bite the animal. A Komodo dragon can bring down a water buffalo.

Komodo dragons live in the wild on four islands in the country of Indonesia. They dig small caves. They spend the daylight hours in these caves or under bushes.

Komodo Dragons

Dragons are scary monsters in stories, legends, and	10
movies. But have you ever wondered whether they were real?	20

Imagine heading out for a day of fishing. You see | 30
an island that looks like a good fishing spot. As you | 41
approach the island, you see creatures bigger than your | 50
small fishing boat that look like dragons. | 57

In 1912, a group of fishermen who went to Komodo | 67
Island had a frightening experience just like the one | 76
described. They spotted huge creatures that looked like | 84
dragons. The fishermen told their dragon stories when | 92
they returned home, but the stories did not get a lot of | 104
attention. | 105

In 1926, the American Museum of Natural History | 113
sponsored a trip to Komodo. The expedition confirmed | 121
that the fishermen's stories were true. They studied the | 130
creatures and called them Komodo dragons. | 136

A Komodo dragon is the largest living lizard. Grown | 145
Komodo dragons are between seven and nine feet long | 154
and weigh between 150 and 300 pounds. | 161

Komodo dragons eat meat. They hunt small deer | 169
and wild pigs by hiding in the grass and waiting. Then | 180
they lean out and bite the animal. A Komodo dragon | 190
can bring down a water buffalo. | 196

Komodo dragons live in the wild on four islands | 205
in the country of Indonesia. They dig small caves. They | 215
spend the daylight hours in these caves or under bushes. | 225

_____ / WCPM

Lewis and Clark

In 1804, President Thomas Jefferson asked Meriwether Lewis to lead a daring expedition beyond the western frontier. Lewis chose his friend William Clark to be his partner. Together, they chose a group of about 40 men with good wilderness skills to find a safe water route to the Pacific Ocean. Jefferson called this group the "Corps of Discovery." The word *corps* means "a group of people with a common goal."

Lewis was the perfect choice to lead the Corps of Discovery. He designed the main riverboat himself to make sure that it had room to store everything they needed for the journey. During the trip, Captain Lewis recorded excellent details in a journal nearly every day.

Clark was the chief mapmaker for the expedition. He drew 60 maps of places they explored. He sketched the Great Falls of the Missouri River in his journal.

They traveled 7,600 miles and faced many difficulties along the way. Traveling over the Rocky Mountains was a hard part of the trip. A bitter, cold winter made it hard to find food and water. They were tired and hungry when they came out of the mountains. Luckily the Corps met Native Americans who fed them and showed them how to build canoes.

Although they never found a water route to the ocean, Lewis and Clark opened the American frontier. They mapped large parts of the West and blazed new trails.

Lewis and Clark

In 1804, President Thomas Jefferson asked
Meriwether Lewis to lead a daring expedition beyond
the western frontier. Lewis chose his friend William
Clark to be his partner. Together, they chose a group of
about 40 men with good wilderness skills to find a safe
water route to the Pacific Ocean. Jefferson called this
group the "Corps of Discovery." The word *corps* means
"a group of people with a common goal."

Lewis was the perfect choice to lead the Corps
of Discovery. He designed the main riverboat himself
to make sure that it had room to store everything they
needed for the journey. During the trip, Captain Lewis
recorded excellent details in a journal nearly every day.

Clark was the chief mapmaker for the expedition.
He drew 60 maps of places they explored. He sketched
the Great Falls of the Missouri River in his journal.

They traveled 7,600 miles and faced many
difficulties along the way. Traveling over the Rocky
Mountains was a hard part of the trip. A bitter, cold
winter made it hard to find food and water. They were
tired and hungry when they came out of the mountains.
Luckily the Corps met Native Americans who fed them
and showed them how to build canoes.

Although they never found a water route to the
ocean, Lewis and Clark opened the American frontier.
They mapped large parts of the West and blazed new trails.

	3
	9
	17
	25
	36
	47
	56
	65
	73
	82
	90
	101
	110
	119
	127
	137
	147
	154
	162
	173
	184
	194
	203
	210
	219
	227
	238

_____ / WCPM

A Team Effort

Tony searched for his brother Luke in the school auditorium's audience. While he looked, Tony revisited the day that could have ruined his basketball career.

Tony had climbed a tree to retrieve a cap that a gust of wind had carried away. He lost his balance and tumbled to the ground. As he felt a terrible pain in his leg, he hoped that his days of playing basketball weren't over.

Tony's right leg was broken in several places. While Tony's leg was healing, Luke brought home Tony's schoolwork each day and tutored him so he wouldn't fall behind. Luke drove Tony to the physical therapy clinic three afternoons a week and helped him do the painful exercises. When Tony got discouraged, Luke encouraged him. He promised Tony he would work with him until he was back playing basketball.

Gradually Tony's leg became stronger. He was ready when the basketball season started. Luke came to the gym every afternoon and massaged and stretched Tony's leg before practice. Soon Tony was playing better than ever, and he started in almost every game. After the team won the championship, Tony's teammates voted him the most valuable player on the team.

When Tony went to the stage to receive his award, he planned to give a most valuable player award of his own. He may have starred on the basketball court, but the real star was his brother Luke.

A Team Effort

	3

Tony searched for his brother Luke in the school | 12

auditorium's audience. While he looked, Tony revisited | 19

the day that could have ruined his basketball career. | 28

Tony had climbed a tree to retrieve a cap that a | 39

gust of wind had carried away. He lost his balance and | 50

tumbled to the ground. As he felt a terrible pain in his | 62

leg, he hoped that his days of playing basketball weren't | 72

over. | 73

Tony's right leg was broken in several places. | 81

While Tony's leg was healing, Luke brought home Tony's | 90

schoolwork each day and tutored him so he wouldn't fall | 100

behind. Luke drove Tony to the physical therapy clinic | 109

three afternoons a week and helped him do the painful | 119

exercises. When Tony got discouraged, Luke encouraged | 126

him. He promised Tony he would work with him until | 136

he was back playing basketball. | 141

Gradually Tony's leg became stronger. He was | 148

ready when the basketball season started. Luke came to | 157

the gym every afternoon and massaged and stretched | 165

Tony's leg before practice. Soon Tony was playing better | 174

than ever, and he started in almost every game. After the | 185

team won the championship, Tony's teammates voted | 192

him the most valuable player on the team. | 200

When Tony went to the stage to receive his award, | 210

he planned to give a most valuable player award of his | 221

own. He may have starred on the basketball court, but | 231

the real star was his brother Luke. | 238

_____ / WCPM

Diagnostic Assessments

Cat

7

A girl found a red ball.

B

Pigs

The pigs live in a pen.

The pigs like mud!

A big pig digs in the mud.

Do you like pigs?

wonderful   **won**

in   **introduction**

tell   **television**

Chrysanthemums   **Chris**

Print Concepts Inventory

To administer the Print Concepts Inventory, you will need a suitable trade book that contains a combination of pictures and text. You will also need the two Print Concept Blackline Master pages 33–34 from this book. The directions for administering this assessment can be found on T16–T19.

	Task	Goal	Score
Parts of a book (1 point for each task)	1. Identifying the front of a book		
	2. Identifying the back of a book	3 out of 3	_____ /3
	3. Identifying the title page of a book		
	4. Identifying the title of a book		
	5. Identifying an author	3 out of 3	_____ /3
	6. Identifying an illustrator		
Purpose of Print			
Blackline Master page 33 (1 point for each task)	7. Distinguish a number		
	8. Distinguish a letter		
	9. Distinguish a word	5 out of 5	_____ /5
	10. Distinguish the first letter of a word		
	11. Distinguish the last letter of a word		
	12. Distinguish a sentence		
	13. Distinguish the first word of a sentence	3 out of 3	_____ /3
	14. Identify spacing between words		
Blackline Master page 34 (1 point for each task)	15. Identify a title		
	16. Where to start reading		
	17. Reading from left to right	5 out of 5	_____ /5
	18. Return sweep		
	19. Reading from top to bottom		
	20. Capitalization		
	21. Identifying a period		
	22. Identifying a question mark	4 out of 4	_____ /4
	23. Identifying an exclamation point		
	24. Word hunt: *like*	1 out of 1	_____ /1
(1 point for each task)	25. Spoken/Written word correspondence	3 out of 4	_____ /4

Total Correct _____ /28

v   g   w   e

j   a   r   b

n   i   k   x

y   c   m   d

u   l   f   t

z   o   h   p

s   q

Name _____ Date _____

Letter-Sound Fluency
Administering and Recording Form

Say: *I am going to point to a letter and then you will tell me the sound that letter makes.*

Point to each letter. Pause and wait for the child to respond. If the child tells you a letter name, remind the child to tell you the sound, not the letter.

Letter-Sound	Child's Response	Letter-Sound	Child's Response	Letter-Sound	Child's Response	Letter-Sound	Child's Response
v /v/		g /g/		w /w/		e /e/	
j /j/		a /a/		r /r/		b /b/	
n /n/		i /i/		k /k/		x /ks/	
y /y/		c /k/		m /m/		d /d/	
u /u/		l /l/		f /f/		t /t/	
z /z/		o /o/		h /h/		p /p/	
s /s/		q /kw/					

Total Correct: _____ /26

Phonological Awareness Inventory

Words in a Sentence
Administering and Recording Form

Task: The child will listen to a sentence and identify the number of words in the sentence.

Model: **Say:** *I am going to say a sentence. I want you to repeat the sentence and clap to show me each word you hear in the sentence. Let's do one together.* **I like to jump.** Repeat the sentence, clapping once for each word. Be sure to articulate each word separately. *We clapped our hands four times because there are four words in the sentence.*

Sample: **Then say:** *Now you try one. After I say the sentence, you say it. Then clap to show me each word you hear in the sentence.* **She runs fast.** Pause and wait for the child to respond. (3) *You're correct. You clapped your hands three times.* If the child misses the task, demonstrate the correct answer.

Then say: *Now listen to some more sentences. Repeat each sentence and clap your hands for each word you hear.*

Sentence	Correct Response	Child's Response
1. Look out.	2	
2. She is sad.	3	
3. The fan is on.	4	
4. I like cats.	3	
5. They will have fun.	4	
6. Come here.	2	
7. You can do it.	4	
8. We sing songs.	3	
9. The frog hops and hops.	5	
10. He can jump up.	4	

Score: _____ /10

Blend Syllables
Administering and Recording Form

Task: The child will listen to syllables and blend them together to say the word.

Model: **Say:** *I am going to say some word parts. Then I want you to put them together to make a word. I will do the first one. Listen to these word parts:* **cray–on.** *When I put the parts* **cray–on** *together, they make the word* **crayon.**

Sample: **Then say:** *Now you try one. Listen to these word parts:* **fast–er.** *What word do you make when you put* **fast–er** *together?* Pause and wait for the child to respond. *(faster) You're correct. The word parts* **fast–er** *make the word* **faster.**

Then say: *Now listen to some more word parts. You put the word parts together to make a word and tell me the word.*

Word	Correct Response	Child's Response
1. pop–corn	popcorn	
2. ham–mer	hammer	
3. lem–on	lemon	
4. min–ute	minute	
5. side–walk	sidewalk	
6. play–pen	playpen	
7. tar–get	target	
8. back–pack	backpack	
9. an-oth-er	another	
10. tel–e–phone	telephone	

Score: _____ /10

Segment Syllables
Administering and Recording Form

Task: The child will listen to a word and identify the number of syllables.

Model: **Say:** *I am going to say a word. I want you to repeat the word and clap to show the parts, or syllables, you hear. Watch me first:* **teacher.** *Repeat the word, clapping hands once for each syllable. Be sure to articulate each syllable clearly.* **Teacher** *has two syllables.*

Sample: **Then say:** *Now you try one. After I say the word, you say it. Clap to show me each part, or syllable, you hear in the word:* **rainbow.** *Pause and wait for the child to respond. (2) You're correct.* **Rainbow** *has two syllables. If the child misses the task, demonstrate the correct answer.*

Then say: *Now listen to some more words. Repeat each word and clap your hands for each part, or syllable, you hear.*

Word	Correct Response	Child's Response
1. kitchen	2	
2. that	1	
3. mitten	2	
4. butterfly	3	
5. purse	1	
6. wagon	2	
7. playroom	2	
8. waterfall	3	
9. book	1	
10. funny	2	

Score: _____ /10

Delete Syllables
Administering and Recording Form

Task: The child will listen to a word and delete a syllable to create a new word.

Model: **Say:** *Listen to this word:* **downtown**. *If I take off the first word part,* **down**, *the new word is* **town**.

Sample: **Then say:** *Now you try one. Listen to this word:* **outside**. *If you take off the first word part,* **out**, *what will the new word be?* Pause and wait for the child to respond. *(side)* You're correct. The new word is **side**.

Then say: *Now listen to some more words. Take off the first word part in each word, and tell me what the new word is.*

Word	Correct Response	Child's Response
1. sunset (sun)	set	
2. anyway (any)	way	
3. uphill (up)	hill	
4. bedroom (bed)	room	
5. doghouse (dog)	house	
6. football (foot)	ball	
7. into (in)	to	
8. seaside (sea)	side	
9. ahead (a)	head	
10. grandson (grand)	son	

Score: _____ /10

Recognize Rhyming Words
Administering and Recording Form

Task: The child will listen to a word and recognize a word that rhymes with it.

Model: **Say:** *Let's play a word game. Listen to these two words:* **bat**, **mat**. *They are rhyming words because they end with the same sounds.*

Sample: **Then say:** *Now you tell me, does* **mop** *rhyme with* **top**? *Pause and wait for the child to respond.* (Yes) *You're correct.* **Mop** *and* **top** *rhyme because they end with the same sounds. Let's try another one. Does* **pin** *rhyme with* **jug**? *Pause and wait for the child to respond.* (No) *You're correct.* **Pin** *and* **jug** *do not rhyme because they do not end with the same sounds.*

Then say: *Now listen to some more words. I will say two words and you tell me if they rhyme.*

Words	Correct Response	Child's Response
1. cap, map	Yes	
2. dig, wig	Yes	
3. pet, miss	No	
4. cut, nut	Yes	
5. sail, note	No	
6. coat, home	No	
7. fun, sun	Yes	
8. camp, lamp	Yes	
9. bone, boss	No	
10. house, mouse	Yes	

Score: _____ /10

Produce Rhyming Words
Administering and Recording Form

Task: The child will listen to a word and produce a word that rhymes with it.

Model: **Say:** *Let's play a word game. Listen to these two words:* **sit, bit**. *They are rhyming words because they end with the same sounds.*

Sample: **Then say:** *Now you tell me a word that rhymes with* **gate** *(date, late, plate). If the child cannot produce a rhyming word, model a correct response.* Let's try another one. *Tell me a word that rhymes with* **seal**. *Pause and wait for the child to respond. Accept any word that rhymes with* **seal** *(deal, meal, real). If the child cannot produce a rhyming word, model a correct response.*

Then say: *Now listen to some more words. I will say a word and you tell me a word that rhymes with it.*

Word	Correct Response	Child's Response
1. cap	lap, nap, tap	
2. same	came, game, tame	
3. fly	my, sky, by	
4. wet	get, bet, set	
5. fun	one, sun, run	
6. stop	hop, pop, top	
7. night	right, bite, light	
8. boat	coat, goat, note	
9. fan	man, ran, can	
10. red	fed, bed, said	

Score: _____ /10

Categorize Rhyming Words
Administering and Recording Form

Task: The child will listen to a series of words and use categorizing skills to determine which word does not rhyme with the others.

Model: **Say:** *Let's play a word game. Listen to these words:* **man, fan, sit**. *Not all of these words rhyme.* **Sit** *does not rhyme with the other words because it does not have the same ending sound as* **man** *and* **fan**.

Sample: **Then say:** *Now you tell me the word that does not rhyme with the others:* **book, tape, cook**. *Pause and wait for the child to respond.* (tape) *You're correct.* **Tape** *does not rhyme because it does not end with the same sound as* **book** *and* **cook**. *If the child cannot categorize the words to provide the correct answer, provide the correct response, and supply another series of words:* **hid, hop, pop** (hid).

Then say: *Now listen to more words. I will say a list of words and you tell me which word does not rhyme with the others.*

Words	Correct Response	Child's Response
1. wet, met, sat	sat	
2. kite, line, bite	line	
3. fit, sad, mad	fit	
4. car, need, far, star	need	
5. same, came, game, home	home	

Score: _____ /5

Blend Onset and Rime
Administering and Recording Form

Task: The child will listen to word parts and blend the sounds together to say the word.

Model: **Say:** *I am going to say some word parts. I want you to put them together to make a word. I will do the first one. Listen to these word parts:* **cl–ap.** *When I put the parts* **cl–ap** *together, they make the word* **clap.**

Sample: **Then say:** *Listen to these word parts:* **m–et.** *What word do you make when you put* **m–et** *together?* Pause and wait for the child to respond. (met) *You're correct. They make the word* **met.**

Then say: *Now listen again. I will say some more word parts. You put them together to make a word and tell me the word.*

Word	Correct Response	Child's Response
1. sh–ip	ship	
2. b–ell	bell	
3. c–ar	car	
4. l–amp	lamp	
5. f–eet	feet	
6. r–ice	rice	
7. h–and	hand	
8. t–all	tall	
9. b–oat	boat	
10. d–ish	dish	

Score: _____ /10

Segment Onset and Rime
Administering and Recording Form

Task: The child will listen to a word and delete the beginning word sound to create a new word.

Model: **Say:** *Listen to this word:* **bad**. *If I have the word* **bad** *and I take off the first word sound,* **/b/**, *the new word is* **add**.

Sample: **Then say:** *Now you try one. Listen to this word:* **sit**. *If you take off the first word sound,* **/s/**, *what will the new word be? Pause and wait for the child to respond.* (it) *You're correct. The new word is* **it**.

Then say: *Now listen to some more words. I will take off the first word sound in each word, and you tell me what the new word is.*

Word	Correct Response	Child's Response
1. /f/ fox	ox	
2. /g/ gate	ate	
3. /b/ ball	all	
4. /l/ land	and	
5. /k/ cold	old	
6. /m/ mice	ice	
7. /s/ send	end	
8. /r/ ran	an	
9. /p/ pup	up	
10. /sh/ shape	ape	

Score: _____ /10

Name _____ Date _____

Isolate Initial Sound
Administering and Recording Form

Task: The child will listen to a word and produce the initial phoneme in the word.

Model: **Say:** *I am going to say a word. Then I am going to say just the beginning sound. Listen carefully for the beginning sound:* **nose.** *The beginning sound is /n/.*

Sample: **Then say:** *Listen to another word. This time you tell me the beginning sound. Listen carefully:* **hand.** *What is the beginning sound in* **hand**? Pause and wait for the child to respond. (/h/) *You're correct. /h/ is the beginning sound in* **hand.** *If the child tells you a letter name, remind the child to tell you the sound, not the letter.*

Then say: *Now listen to some more words. Tell me the beginning sound you hear in each word.*

Word	Correct Response	Child's Response
1. name	/n/	
2. bunny	/b/	
3. farm	/f/	
4. door	/d/	
5. seem	/s/	
6. tape	/t/	
7. purple	/p/	
8. muddy	/m/	
9. goat	/g/	
10. little	/l/	

Score: _____ /10

Isolate Final Sound
Administering and Recording Form

Task: The child will listen to a word and produce the final phoneme in the word.

Model: **Say:** *I am going to say a word. Then I am going to say just the ending sound. Listen carefully for the ending sound:* **tap.** *The ending sound is* **/p/.**

Sample: **Then say:** *Listen to another word. This time you tell me the ending sound. Listen carefully:* **fin.** *What is the ending sound in* **fin?** *Pause and wait for the child to respond. (/n/) You're correct.* **/n/** *is the ending sound in* **fin.** *If the child tells you a letter name, remind the child to tell you the sound, not the letter.*

          Then say: *Now listen to some more words. Tell me the ending sound you hear in each word.*

Word	Correct Response	Child's Response
1. hut	/t/	
2. bug	/g/	
3. head	/d/	
4. like	/k/	
5. gas	/s/	
6. rib	/b/	
7. time	/m/	
8. cup	/p/	
9. mother	/r/	
10. balloon	/n/	

Score: _____ /10

Name _____ Date _____

Isolate Medial Sound
Administering and Recording Form

Task: The child will listen to a word and produce the medial phoneme in the word.

Model: **Say:** *I am going to say a word. Then I am going to say just the middle sound. Listen carefully for the middle sound:* **jet.** *The middle sound is* **/ĕ/.**

Sample: **Then say:** *Listen to another word. This time you tell me the middle sound. Listen carefully:* **lake.** *What is the middle sound in* **lake**? *Pause and wait for the child to respond. (/ā/) You're correct. /ā/ is the middle sound in* **lake.** *If the child tells you a letter name, remind the child to tell you the sound, not the letter.*

Then say: *Now listen to some more words. Tell me the middle sound you hear in each word.*

Word	Correct Response	Child's Response
1. mitt	/ĭ/	
2. pad	/ă/	
3. seat	/ē/	
4. tub	/ŭ/	
5. note	/ō/	
6. fine	/ī/	
7. hop	/ŏ/	
8. deck	/ĕ/	
9. cube	/ū/	
10. name	/ā/	

Score: _____ /10

Identify Phonemes
Administering and Recording Form

Task: The child will listen to a target word's initial phoneme and then listen to a set of words to identify words that have the same initial phoneme.

Model: **Say:** *I am going to say a word. Listen carefully for the beginning sound:* **ball***. Now I am going to say a group of words. Listen for the word that has the same beginning sound as* **ball***. Listen carefully:* **fast, big, top***. The word that has the same beginning sound as* **ball** *is* **big***. The words* **ball** *and* **big** *begin with the same sound,* **/b/***.*

Sample: **Then say:** *Listen to another word,* **fun***. This time you tell me the word that has the same beginning sound as* **fun***. Listen carefully:* **fast, read, jump***. What word has the same beginning sound as* **fun***?* Pause and wait for the child to respond. (fast) *You're correct. The words* **fun** *and* **fast** *both begin with the same sound,* **/f/***.* If the child cannot identify the word, provide the correct answer, name the same beginning sound, and supply another group of words: **hop: line, pat, hid** (hid).

Then say: *Now listen to some more words. Tell me the word that has the same beginning sound as the first word.*

Target Word	Set of Words	Correct Response	Child's Response
1. get	gas, fix, have	gas /g/	
2. pie	we, sand, peel	peel /p/	
3. down	roar, doll, mine	doll /d/	
4. well	wait, milk, seem	wait /w/	
5. nice	sit, fan, need	need /n/	
6. sink	bite, soap, game	soap /s/	
7. hill	house, band, sad	house /h/	
8. man	roam, paint, make	make /m/	
9. read	nap, rip, dine	rip /r/	
10. kite	tall, cat, hug	cat /k/	

Score: _____ /10

Name _____ Date _____

Categorize Phonemes
Administering and Recording Form

Task: The child will listen to three words and identify the word that has an initial phoneme that is different from the other two.

Model: **Say:** *I am going to say three words. Listen carefully for the beginning sound in each word:* **foot, like, find.** *Which word has a different beginning sound than the other two:* **foot, like, find**? **Like** *begins with a different sound than* **foot** *and* **find.**

Sample: **Then say:** *Listen to three more words. This time you tell me the word that begins with a different sound than the other two. Listen carefully:* **sock, road, seat.** *Which word has a different beginning sound than the other two:* **sock, road, seat**? Pause and wait for the child to respond. (road) *You're correct.* **Road** *begins with a different sound than* **sock** *and* **seat.**

Then say: *Now listen to some more words. Tell me the word in each group that has a different beginning sound.*

Words	Correct Response	Child's Response
1. cab, cup, mice	mice	
2. bean, heart, base	heart	
3. next, jump, jet	next	
4. leg, house, lunch	house	
5. duck, pin, pace	duck	
6. move, bow, mine	bow	
7. fly, go, guess	fly	
8. mother, make, leaf	leaf	
9. ring, dig, deep.	ring	
10. night, send, now	send	

Score: _____ /10

Blend Phonemes
Administering and Recording Form

Task: The child will listen to individual sounds and blend the sounds together to say the word.

Model: **Say:** *I am going to say some sounds. Then I want you to put them together to make a word. I will do the first one. Listen to these sounds: /m/–/ă/–/p/. When I put the sounds /m/–/ă/–/p/ together, they make the word* **map.**

Sample: **Then say:** *Listen to these sounds: /n/–/ŏ/–/t/. What word do you make when you put /n/–/ŏ/–/t/ together? Pause and wait for the child to respond. (not) You're correct. The sounds /n/–/ŏ/–/t/ make the word* **not.**

           Then say: *Now listen again. I will say some sounds. Put the sounds together to make a word, and tell me the word.*

Word	Correct Response	Child's Response
1. /p/–/ĕ/–/t/	pet	
2. /l/–/ă/–/n/–/d/	land	
3. /h/–/ŭ/–/g/	hug	
4. /b/–/ĕ/–/d/	bed	
5. /m/–/ŭ/–/s/–/t/	must	
6. /d/–/ŏ/–/t/	dot	
7. /k/–/ŭ/–/p/	cup	
8. /d/–/ĭ/–/g/	dig	
9. /r/–/ă/–/m/–/p/	ramp	
10. /s/–/ē/	see	

Score: _____ /10

Name _____ Date _____

Segment Phonemes
Administering and Recording Form

Task: The child will listen to a word and produce each phoneme in the word separately.

Model: **Say:** *I am going to say a word. Then I am going to say each sound. Listen carefully for each sound. The word is* **low**. *The sounds in* **low** *are /l/–/ō/.* Be sure to articulate each sound separately. Do not simply stretch out the word.

Sample: **Then say:** *Listen to this word. This time you tell me the sounds in the word. Listen carefully:* **bet**. *What sounds do you hear in* **bet**? Pause and wait for child to respond. *(/b/–/ĕ/–/t/)* *You're correct. The sounds* **/b/–/ĕ/–/t/** *make the word* **bet**.

Then say: *Now listen to some more words. Tell me each sound you hear in these words.*

Word	Correct Response	Child's Response
1. up	/ŭ/–/p/	
2. hen	/h/–/ĕ/–/n/	
3. man	/m/–/ă/–/n/	
4. beep	/b/–/ē/–/p/	
5. road	/r/–/ō/–/d/	
6. it	/ĭ/–/t/	
7. hike	/h/–/ī/–/k/	
8. jig	/j/–/ĭ/–/g/	
9. fun	/f/–/ŭ/–/n/	
10. face	/f/–/ā/–/s/	

Score: _____ /10

Delete Phonemes
Administering and Recording Form

Task: The child will listen to a word and delete a phoneme from the word to create a new word.

Model: **Say:** *Listen to this word: rice. If I take off the /r/ sound, the new word will be ice.*

Sample: **Then say:** *Now you try one. Listen to this word: jam. If you take off the /j/ sound, what will the new word be?* Pause and wait for the child to respond. (am) *You're correct. The new word is am.*

           Then say: *Now listen to some more words and tell me what the new words will be when a sound is deleted.*

Word	Correct Response	Child's Response
1. cold /k/	old	
2. race /r/	ace	
3. feel /f/	eel	
4. mat /m/	at	
5. win /w/	in	
6. neat /n/	eat	
7. rake /k/	ray	
8. beep /p/	bee	
9. nose /s/	no	
10. seed /d/	see	

Score: _____ /10

Add Phonemes
Administering and Recording Form

Task: The child will listen to a word and add a phoneme to the word to create
          a new word.

Model: **Say:** *Listen to this sound: /b/. If I add the /b/ sound to the word* **at**, *the new
         word will be* **bat**.

Sample: **Then say:** *Now you try one. Listen to this sound: /h/. If you add the sound /h/ to
         the word* **ill**, *what will the new word be? Pause and wait for the child to respond.
         (hill) You're correct. The new word will be* **hill**. *Sometimes a sound may be added
         to the end of the word. If you have the word* **say** *and the sound /m/ is added
         to the end, what will the new word be? Pause and wait for the child to respond.
         (same) You're correct. The new word is* **same**.

         Then say: *Now listen to some more words and tell me what the new words will
         be when a sound is added.*

Word	Correct Response	Child's Response
1. /m/ ice	mice	
2. /s/ it	sit	
3. /k/ up	cup	
4. /b/ all	ball	
5. /f/ ox	fox	
6. /m/ any	many	
7. /g/ oat	goat	
8. we /k/	week	
9. day /t/	date	
10. lie /f/	life	

Score: _____ /10

Name _____ Date _____

Substitute Phonemes
Administering and Recording Form

Task: The child will listen to a word and replace either the initial or final phoneme from the word to create a new word.

Model: **Say:** *I am going to say a word. I want you to take off the first sound of the word and put in a new sound. For example, if I change the first sound in **cap** to /l/ the new word is **lap**. Sometimes I'll ask you to take off the ending sound and put in a new sound. If I change the last sound in the word **web** to /t/, the new word is **wet**.*

Sample: **Then say:** *Now you try one. Change the first sound in **met** to /p/. What will the new word be? Pause and wait for the child to respond. (pet) You're correct. The new word is **pet**. Now try another one. Change the last sound in **hat** to /z/. What will the new word be? Pause and wait for the child to respond. (has) You're correct. The new word is **has**.*

Then say: *Now listen to some more words. Tell me the new words you will make.*

Word	Correct Response	Child's Response
Initial Sounds		
1. /s/ lick	sick	
2. /n/ mail	nail	
3. /f/ tan	fan	
4. /h/ dive	hive	
5. /b/ fed	bed	
Final Sounds		
6. ten /l/	tell	
7. rode /z/	rose	
8. lime /k/	like	
9. run /g/	rug	
10. make /d/	made	

Score: _____ /10

Progress-Monitoring Assessments

Kindergarten
Progress-Monitoring
Assessments
Forms 1–15

1

B   c   e   D   b   A

f   J   G   i   h   g

K   o   l   m   L   N

2

t   s   c

3

I like   .

I like   .

Phonemic Awareness: Segment Phonemes

Goal: 3/3 Score: _____ /3

Say, *sat.* What sounds do you hear in *sat*?

sat   sun   pan

/s/ /ă/ /t/ _____   /s/ /ŭ/ /n/ _____   /p/ /ă/ /n/ _____

Letter Naming

Goal: 15/18 Score: _____ /18

1

B	c	e	D	b	A
f	J	G	i	h	g
K	o	l	m	L	N

Letter-Sound Relationships

Goal: 3/3 Score: _____ /3

2

t   s   c

Say, *cap.* Which letter stands for the sound at the beginning of *cap*?

Say, *sat.* Which letter stands for the sound at the beginning of *sat*?

Say, *tap.* Which letter stands for the sound at the beginning of *tap*?

Sentence Reading

Goal: 4/4 Score: _____ /4

3

I like [grapes] .

I like [bananas] .

1

P   t   s   R

Q   v   u   X

Z   w   y

2

m   p   a

3

the   like   I   and

4

I like the 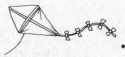 .

I like the .

Phonemic Awareness: Segment Phonemes

Goal: 3/3 Score: _____ /3

Say, *ant.* What sound do you hear in *ant*?

ant   tap   mat

/ă/ /n/ /t/ _____   /t/ /ă/ /p/ _____   /m/ /ă/ /t/ _____

Letter Naming

Goal: 8/11 Score: _____ /11

1

P	t	s	R
Q	v	u	X
Z	w	y	

Letter-Sound Relationships

Goal: 3/3 Score: _____ /3

2

m   p   a

Say, *at.* Which letter stands for the sound at the beginning of *at*?

Say, *map.* Which letter stands for the sound at the beginning of *map*?

Say, *pat.* Which letter stands for the sound at the beginning of *pat*?

High-Frequency Words

Goal: 4/4 Score: _____ /4

3

the   like   I   and

Sentence Reading

Goal: 5/6 Score: _____ /6

4

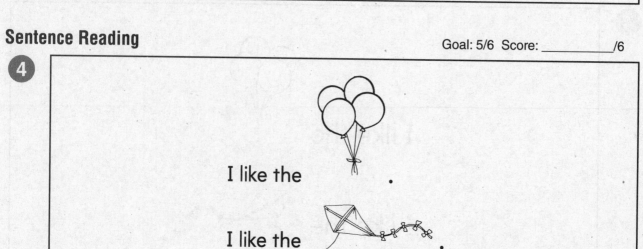

I like the ____ .

I like the ____ .

1

s   m   a

2

see   we   a   to   like   I   the   and

3

I see a ⚽ .

We like to _____ .

Phonemic Awareness: Segment Phonemes

Goal: 3/3 Score: _____/3

Say, *sit.* What sounds do you hear in *sit*?

sit   eat   road

/s/ /ĭ/ /t/ _____   /ē/ /t/ _____   /r/ /ō/ /d/ _____

Letter-Sound Relationships

Goal: 3/3 Score: _____/3

s	m	a

Say, *sun.* Which letter stands for the sound at the beginning of *sun*?

Say, *ant.* Which letter stands for the sound at the beginning of *ant*?

Say, *map.* Which letter stands for the sound at the beginning of *map*?

High-Frequency Words

Goal: 7/8 Score: _____/8

see	we	a	to	like	I	the	and

Sentence Reading

Goal: 5/6 Score: _____/6

I see a  .

We like to  .

1

c t m a s p

2

come me we a see to

3

mat sap cat tap sat map pat cap

4

We see a .

We like the .

We come to .

Phonemic Awareness: Segment Phonemes

Goal: 3/3 Score: _____ /3

Say, *tap.* What sounds do you hear in *tap*?

tap	kick	run
/t/ /ă/ /p/ _____	/k/ /ĭ/ /k/ _____	/r/ /ŭ/ /n/ _____

Letter-Sound Relationships

Goal: 3/3 Score: _____ /3

1

c   t   m   a   s   p

Say, *ten.* Which letter stands for the sound at the beginning of *ten*?

Say, *mix.* Which letter stands for the sound at the beginning of *mix*?

Say, *ask.* Which letter stands for the sound at the beginning of *ask*?

High-Frequency Words

Goal: 5/6 Score: _____ /6

2

come   me   we   a   see   to

Decodable Words

Goal: 7/8 Score: _____ /8

3

mat   sap   cat   tap   sat   map   pat   cap

Sentence Reading

Goal: 8/9 Score: _____ /9

4

We see a _____ .

We like the _____ .

We come to _____ .

1

f n c m a p

2

my with you what we come like see

3

man nap fan pat sat pan can fat tap fast

4

I like my hat.

Come with me.

What can you see?

Progress-Monitoring Assessments
SESSIONS K.74A, K.74B,
K.75A, K.75B

Phonemic Awareness: Segment Phonemes

Goal: 3/3 Score: _____/3

Say, *map.* What sounds do you hear in *map*?

man   up   fun

/m/ /ă/ /n/ _____   /ŭ/ /p/ _____   /f/ /ŭ/ /n/ _____

Letter-Sound Relationships

Goal: 3/3 Score: _____/3

1

f	n	c	m	a	p

Say, *fan.* Which letter stands for the sound at the beginning of *fan*?

Say, *nap.* Which letter stands for the sound at the beginning of *nap*?

Say, *man.* Which letter stands for the sound at the beginning of *man*?

High-Frequency Words

Goal: 7/8 Score: _____/8

2

my	with	you	what	we	come	like	see

Decodable Words

Goal: 8/10 Score: _____/10

3

man	nap	fan	pat	sat	pan	can	fat	tap	fast

Sentence Reading

Goal: 9/11 Score: _____/11

4

I like my hat.

Come with me.

What can you see?

1

b   a   s   n   p   c

2

are   now   you   what   my   with   come   me

3

at   tap   am   nap   bat   cab   pat   ban   tab   fat

4

What can you see?

Come with me now.

Are you with Pam?

Phonemic Awareness: Segment Phonemes

Goal: 3/3 Score: _____/3

Say, *pan.* What sounds do you hear in *pan*?

pan	it	race
/p/ /ă/ /n/ _____	/ĭ/ /t/ _____	/r/ /ā/ /s/ _____

Letter-Sound Relationships

Goal: 3/3 Score: _____/3

1

b	a	s	n	p	c

Say, *nap.* What letter is at the beginning of the word *nap*?

Say, *bat.* What letter is at the beginning of the word *bat*?

Say, *cab.* What letter is at the beginning of the word *cab*?

High-Frequency Words

Goal: 7/8 Score: _____/8

2

are	now	you	what	my	with	come	me

Decodable Words

Goal: 8/10 Score: _____/10

3

at	tap	am	nap	bat	cab	pat	ban	tab	fat

Sentence Reading

Goal: 10/12 Score: _____/12

4

What can you see?

Come with me now.

Are you with Pam?

1

b   i   p   n   f   g

2

many is how where this from came find

3

fin big gas fit bag nap sag sip in pig

4

This is a big pig.

Where is Tim from?

How many cats can we find?

Phonemic Awareness: Segment Phonemes

Goal: 3/3 Score: _____/3

Say, *hut*. What sounds do you hear in *hut*?

hut   beep   top

/h/ /ŭ/ /t/ _____   /b/ /ē/ /p/ _____   /t/ /ŏ/ /p/ _____

Letter-Sound Relationships

Goal: 3/3 Score: _____/3

1

| b | i | p | n | f | g |

Say, *big*. What letter is at the beginning of the word *big*?

Say, *gap*. What letter is at the beginning of the word *gap*?

Say, *in*. What letter is at the beginning of the word *in*?

High-Frequency Words

Goal: 7/8 Score: _____/8

2

| many | is | how | where | this | from | came | find |

Decodable Words

Goal: 8/10 Score: _____/10

3

| fin | big | gas | fit | bag | nap | sag | sip | in | pig |

Sentence Reading

Goal: 13/15 Score: _____/15

4

This is a big pig.

Where is Tim from?

How many cats can we find?

1

d   r   f   i   g   b

2

will   here   your   who   go   they   soon   be

3

rip   in   big   gap   fin   bad   dip   rat   rib   tag

4

Who is Dan?

They will be here soon.

We will dig your pit.

Phonemic Awareness: Segment Phonemes

Goal: 3/3 Score: _____/3

Say, *see.* What sounds do you hear in *see*?

see	dog	fun
/s/ /ē/ _____	/d/ /ŏ/ /g/ _____	/f/ /ŭ/ /n/ _____

Letter-Sound Relationships

Goal: 3/3 Score: _____/3

1

d	r	f	i	g	b

Say, *rib.* What letter is at the beginning of the word *rib*?

Say, *did.* What letter is at the beginning of the word *did*?

Say, *fig.* What letter is at the beginning of the word *fig*?

High-Frequency Words

Goal: 7/8 Score: _____/8

2

will	here	your	who	go	they	soon	be

Decodable Words

Goal: 8/10 Score: _____/10

3

rip	in	big	gap	fin	bad	dip	rat	rib	tag

Sentence Reading

Goal: 11/13 Score: _____/13

4

Who is Dan?

They will be here soon.

We will dig your pit.

1

g   d   r   o   f   i

2

make   play   them   give   say   new   here   soon

3

rat   dot   gap   bag   rip   mop   rod   dim   fit   tag

4

Give them the mop.

Here is the new pot.

Ron will play hop on top.

Phonemic Awareness: Segment Phonemes

Goal: 3/3 Score: _____/3

Say, *got.* What sounds do you hear in *got*?

got   mop   rod

/g/ /ŏ/ /t/ _____   /m/ / ŏ / /p/ _____   /r/ / ŏ / /d/ _____

Letter-Sound Relationships

Goal: 3/3 Score: _____/3

1

g	d	r	o	f	i

Say, *dig.* What letter is at the beginning of the word *dig?*

Say, *on.* What letter is at the beginning of the word of *on*?

Say, *rob.* What letter is at the beginning of the word of *rob*?

High-Frequency Words

Goal: 7/8 Score: _____/8

2

make	play	them	give	say	new	here	soon

Decodable Words

Goal: 8/10 Score: _____/10

3

rat	dot	gap	bag	rip	mop	rod	dim	fit	tag

Sentence Reading

Goal: 13/15 Score: _____/15

4

Give them the mop.

Here is the new pot.

Ron will play hop on top.

1

x   r   d   e   n   j

2

said   good   was   ate   could   she   all   when

3

mix   jog   red   job   hop   fox   jet   dog   fed   box

4

Jen fed the dog.

She did a good job.

Could you mix all of this?

A red fox ate the box.

Name _____ Date _____

Phonemic Awareness: Segment Phonemes

Goal: 3/3 Score: _____ /3

Say, *rat.* What sounds do you hear in *rat?*

rat   fox   mail

/r/ /ă/ /t/ _____   /f/ /ŏ/ /x/ _____   /m/ /ā/ /l/ _____

Letter-Sound Relationships

Goal: 3/3 Score: _____ /3

1

x	r	d	e	n	j

Say, *jet.* What letter is at the beginning of the word *jet?*

Say, *egg.* What letter is at the beginning of the word *egg?*

Say, *next.* What letter is at the beginning of the word *next?*

High-Frequency Words

Goal: 7/8 Score: _____ /8

2

said	good	was	ate	could	she	all	when

Decodable Words

Goal: 8/10 Score: _____ /10

3

mix	jog	red	job	hop	fox	jet	dog	fed	box

Sentence Reading

Goal: 19/21 Score: _____ /21

4

Jen fed the dog.

She did a good job.

Could you mix all of this?

A red fox ate the box.

1

h   e   o   x   k   j

2

no he away must by there then over

3

fox jam hen kid ox hem kit fix hop box

4

He is over there.

Ken must fix the bed.

The hen ran away.

No, the mop is by the box.

Phonemic Awareness: Segment Phonemes

Goal: 3/3 Score: _____ /3

Say, *hop.* What sounds do you hear in *hop*?

hop   .   hen   kit

/h/ /ŏ / /p/ _____   /h/ /ĕ / /n/ _____   /k/ /ĭ / /t/ _____

Letter-Sound Relationships

Goal: 3/3 Score: _____ /3

1

| h | e | o | x | k | j |

Say, *hot.* What letter is at the beginning of the word *hot*?

Say, *egg.* What letter is at the beginning of the word *egg*?

Say, *key.* What letter is at the beginning of the word *key*?

High-Frequency Words

Goal:7/8 Score: _____ /8

2

no   he   away   must   by   there   then   over

Decodable Words

Goal: 8/10 Score: _____ /10

3

fox   jam   hen   kid   ox   hem   kit   fix   hop   box

Sentence Reading

Goal: 18/20 Score: _____ /20

4

He is over there.

Ken must fix the bed.

The hen ran away.

No, the mop is by the box.

1

e o u l w h

2

down went only little just do help walk

3

hen leg tub wet fun ox lap hum wax mud

4

Gus will only walk.

Did you run in the mud?

The little hen got wet.

Let me help you down.

Phonemic Awareness: Segment Phonemes

Goal: 3/3 Score: _____/3

Say, *tub*. What sounds do you hear in *tub*?

tub	let	wig
/t/ /ŭ/ /b/ _____	/l/ /ĕ/ /t/ _____	/w/ /ĭ/ /g/ _____ .

Letter-Sound Relationships

Goal: 3/3 Score: _____/3

1

e	o	u	l	w	h

Say, *up*. What letter is at the beginning of the word *up*?

Say, *land*. What letter is at the beginning of the word *land*?

Say, *win*. What letter is at the beginning of the word *win*?

High-Frequency Words

Goal: 7/8 Score: _____/8

2

down	went	only	little	just	do	help	walk

Decodable Words

Goal: 8/10 Score: _____/10

3

hen	leg	tub	wet	fun	ox	lap	hum	wax	mud

Sentence Reading

Goal: 18/20 Score: _____/20

4

Gus will only walk.

Did you run in the mud?

The little hen got wet.

Let me help you down.

1

v   z   y   q   l   w

2

too   look   out   very   our   day   their   take

3

van zap yes wig yet yam zip win wet quiz

4

Did you zip up yet?

Yes, I got very wet.

Our day was fun, too.

They take their dog to the vet.

Progress-Monitoring Assessments
SESSIONS K.90A, K.90B, K.91A, K.91B

Phonemic Awareness: Segment Phonemes

Goal: 3/3 Score: _____/3

Say, *zap*. What sounds do you hear in *zap*?

zap   note   yet

/z/ /ă/ /p/ _____   /n/ /ō/ /t/ _____   /y/ /ĕ/ /t/ _____

Letter-Sound Relationships

Goal: 3/3 Score: _____/3

1

| v | z | y | q | l | w |

Say, *zip*. What letter is at the beginning of the word *zip*?

Say, *yellow*. What letter is at the beginning of the word *yellow*?

Say, *quit*. What letter is at the beginning of the word *quit*?

High-Frequency Words

Goal: 7/8 Score: _____/8

2

too   look   out   very   our   day   their   take

Decodable Words

Goal: 8/10 Score: _____/10

3

van   zap   yes   wig   yet   yam   zip   win   wet   quiz

Sentence Reading

Goal: 20/22 Score: _____/22

4

Did you zip up yet?

Yes, I got very wet.

Our day was fun, too.

They take their dog to the vet.

1

e   i   u   l   w   y

2

put   saw   off   too   show   look   take   out

3

bite   bit   rip   ripe   be   bet   kit   kite   we   wet

4

I saw the kite rip.

We take out the wet dog.

Did he bite a little bit?

This show will be fun too!

Name _____ Date _____

Phonemic Awareness: Segment Phonemes

Goal: 3/3 Score: _____/3

Say, *bite*. What sounds do you hear in *bite*?

bite _____   met _____   gate _____

/b/ /ī/ /t/ _____   /m/ /ĕ/ /t/ _____   /g/ /ā/ /t/ _____

Letter-Sound Relationships

Goal: 3/3 Score: _____/3

1

| e | i | u | l | w | y |

Say, *up*. What letter is at the beginning of the word *up*?

Say, *we*. What letter is at the beginning of the word *we*?

Say, *lime*. What letter is at the beginning of the word *lime*?

High-Frequency Words

Goal: 7/8 Score: _____/8

2

| put | saw | off | too | show | look | take | out |

Decodable Words

Goal: 8/10 Score: _____/10

3

| bite | bit | rip | ripe | be | bet | kit | kite | we | wet |

Sentence Reading

Goal: 21/23 Score: _____/23

4

I saw the kite rip.

We take out the wet dog.

Did he bite a little bit?

This show will be fun too!

1

a   o   u   e   i   y

2

play give away walk only soon put show

3

tap tape cut cute not note cap cape rob robe

4

Put on your cap and cape.

Do not give away your robe.

Luke will walk home soon.

Can you play the note?

Progress-Monitoring Assessments
SESSIONS K.94A, K.94B, K.94C, K.95

Phonemic Awareness: Segment Phonemes

Goal: 3/3 Score: _____/3

Say, *bug.* What sounds do you hear in *bug*?

bug   rid   line

/b/ /ŭ/ /g/ _____   /r/ /ĭ/ /d/ _____   /l/ /ī/ /n/ _____

Letter-Sound Relationships

Goal: 3/3 Score: _____/3

1

| a | o | u | e | i | y |

Say, *ate.* What letter is at the beginning of the word *ate*?

Say, *old.* What letter is at the beginning of the word *old*?

Say, *yes.* What letter is at the beginning of the word *yes*?

High-Frequency Words

Goal: 7/8 Score: _____/8

2

play   give   away   walk   only   soon   put   show

Decodable Words

Goal: 8/10 Score: _____/10

3

tap   tape   cut   cute   not   note   cap   cape   rob   robe

Sentence Reading

Goal: 20/22 Score: _____/22

4

Put on your cap and cape.

Do not give away your robe.

Luke will walk home soon.

Can you play the note?

Grade 1
Progress-Monitoring
Assessments
Forms 1–18

A.

fan	Dan	fad	nap	pad
dad	tan	pan	sat	Nan

B.

and	be	help
with	you	play

C.

1. Dad and Dan sat.

2. Nan and Dan can help you.

3. Can Dan play with Nan?

Decodable Words

Goal 8/10   Score _____ / 10

A.

fan	Dan	fad	nap	pad
dad	tan	pan	sat	Nan

High-Frequency Words

Goal 5/6   Score _____ / 6

B.

and	be	help
with	you	play

Reading Sentences

Goal 13/15   Score _____ / 15

C.

1. Dad and Dan sat.

2. Nan and Dan can help you.

3. Can Dan play with Nan?

A.

| big | ox | hid | sob | did |
| log | rib | fox | rip | pig |

B.

| funny | sing | they | do | find |
| for | what | have | look | too |

C.

1. They hop and play.

2. He can sing a funny song.

3. What do you have to find?

Decodable Words

Goal 8/10   Score _____ / 10

A.

big	ox	hid	sob	did
log	rib	fox	rip	pig

High-Frequency Words

Goal 8/10   Score _____ / 10

B.

funny	sing	they	do	find
for	what	have	look	too

Reading Sentences

Goal 14/16   Score _____ / 16

C.

1. They hop and play.

2. He can sing a funny song.

3. What do you have to find?

A.

| hen | web | rug | sun | bud |
| hug | jet | yet | jug | vet |

B.

| friend | full | here | hold | good |
| all | many | does | who | pull |

C.

1. Ned and Ken have fun.

2. They get all wet.

3. My friends play and run.

A. Decodable Words

Goal 8/10   Score _____ / 10

hen	web	rug	sun	bud
hug	jet	yet	jug	vet

B. High-Frequency Words

Goal 8/10   Score _____ / 10

friend	full	here	hold	good
all	many	does	who	pull

C. Reading Sentences

Goal 12/14   Score _____ / 14

1. Ned and Ken have fun.

2. They get all wet.

3. My friends play and run.

A.

hut	pack	had	rug	bad
fan	wag	duck	lap	quack

B.

away	call	come	every	who
hear	said	good	pull	my

C.

1. He fell in mud!
2. Jack had no luck.
3. Come away with me.
4. Pack a bag for a friend.

Name _____ Date _____

Decodable Words

Goal 8/10   Score _____ / 10

A.

hut	pack	had	rug	bad
fan	wag	duck	lap	quack

High-Frequency Words

Goal 8/10   Score _____ / 10

B.

away	call	come	every	who
hear	said	good	pull	my

Reading Sentences

Goal 16/18   Score _____ / 18

C.

1. He fell in mud!

2. Jack had no luck.

3. Come away with me.

4. Pack a bag for a friend.

A.

| crib | plan | rip | job | flip |
| clock | top | frog | drip | block |

B.

| how | make | some | why | animal |
| her | now | our | she | today |

C.

1. Can you hear her sing?

2. She would come today.

3. What does a bag hold?

4. Fran can lock it and zip it.

Decodable Words

A.

Goal 8/10   Score _____ / 10

crib	plan	rip	job	flip
clock	top	frog	drip	block

High-Frequency Words

B.

Goal 8/10   Score _____ / 10

how	make	some	why	animal
her	now	our	she	today

Reading Sentences

C.

Goal 18/21   Score _____ / 21

1. Can you hear her sing?

2. She would come today.

3. What does a bag hold?

4. Fran can lock it and zip it.

A.

skin	stop	list	scan	bump
jump	fast	snug	task	nut

B.

after	read	was	write	small
eat	give	put	take	draw

C.

1. You can read and write.

2. Miss Jen can draw pictures.

3. What a funny pup!

4. He has one small snack.

A. Decodable Words

Goal 8/10 Score _____ / 10

skin	stop	list	scan	bump
jump	fast	snug	task	nut

B. High-Frequency Words

Goal 8/10 Score _____ / 10

after	read	was	write	small
eat	give	put	take	draw

C. Reading Sentences

Goal 17/19 Score _____ / 19

1. You can read and write.

2. Miss Jen can draw pictures.

3. What a funny pup!

4. He has one small snack.

A.

| called | Seth | this | bath | catches |
| finds | reading | adds | buzzed | singing |

B.

| water | little | where | far | put |
| cold | blue | one | their | live |

C.

1. Brad hears a little duck.

2. It is eating in the cold water.

3. Where is it?

4. It is here making a fuss.

5. The duck quacks and quacks!

Decodable Words

Goal 8/10   Score _____ / 10

A.

called	Seth	this	bath	catches
finds	reading	adds	buzzed	singing

High-Frequency Words

Goal 8/10   Score _____ / 10

B.

water	little	where	far	put
cold	blue	one	their	live

Reading Sentences

Goal 22/25   Score _____ / 25

C.

1. Brad hears a little duck.

2. It is eating in the cold water.

3. Where is it?

4. It is here making a fuss.

5. The duck quacks and quacks!

A.

itching	Phil's	can't	ship	wish
here's	match	much	when	chop

B.

grow	open	down	new	know
never	off	out	very	yellow

C.

1. Chip goes out to catch a fish.

2. He sits down on a brown bench.

3. He watches the water.

4. Here swims a little fish.

5. Will Chip catch it? We don't know.

Decodable Words   Goal 8/10   Score _____ / 10

A.

itching	Phil's	can't	ship	wish
here's	match	much	when	chop

High-Frequency Words   Goal 8/10   Score _____ / 10

B.

grow	open	down	new	know
never	off	out	very	yellow

Reading Sentences   Goal 26/30 Score _____ / 30

C.

1. Chip goes out to catch a fish.

2. He sits down on a brown bench.

3. He watches the water.

4. Here swims a little fish.

5. Will Chip catch it? We don't know.

A.

fine	edge	comb	cage	sign
wrap	lace	knit	take	cane

B.

long	both	walk	those	into
watch	over	three	five	starts

C.

1. Kate will make a yellow cake.
2. She starts the mix with an egg.
3. Then she puts it in two pans.
4. She walks over to watch it bake.
5. She places the cake down.
6. Let's eat!

Decodable Words   Goal 8/10   Score _____ / 10

A.

fine	edge	comb	cage	sign
wrap	lace	knit	take	cane

High-Frequency Words   Goal 8/10   Score _____ / 10

B.

long	both	walk	those	into
watch	over	three	five	starts

Reading Sentences   Goal 31/34   Score _____ / 34

C.

1. Kate will make a yellow cake.

2. She starts the mix with an egg.

3. Then she puts it in two pans.

4. She walks over to watch it bake.

5. She places the cake down.

6. Let's eat!

A.

hole	tube	huge	fuse	broke
stove	cute	mule	robe	wrote

B.

bring	carry	because	think	those
around	before	light	show	eyes

C.

1. Do you know how to plant roses?
2. Roses come in red, white, and yellow.
3. Some roses are for show.
4. Do roses like to climb up vines?
5. They grow tall if they have a lot of light.
6. Make a note to water the roses.

Decodable Words

Goal 8/10   Score _____ / 10

A.

hole	tube	huge	fuse	broke
stove	cute	mule	robe	wrote

High-Frequency Words

Goal 8/10   Score _____ / 10

B.

bring	carry	because	think	those
around	before	light	show	eyes

Reading Sentences

Goal 38/44   Score _____ / 44

C.

1. Do you know how to plant roses?

2. Roses come in red, white, and yellow.

3. Some roses are just for show.

4. Do roses like to climb up vines?

5. They grow tall if they have a lot of light.

6. Make a note to water the roses.

A.

sing	think	bank	keep	bean
day	stay	rain	leak	he'd

B.

by	car	don't	sure	ground
these	sometimes	under	your	maybe

C.

The Beach

We'll bring your friends to the beach. We will come by car that day. The beach is not far away. It will not take long to get there.

We will bring food for lunch. We can put a sheet on the ground. First we'll sit down and eat.

After lunch, we will walk around. Your friends will see pink sand and clean water. They can swim and play in the waves. They can put sand in their pails. The main thing is to stay out of the deep water.

Maybe they will see a bird dive for fish. The fish will be the bird's lunch.

Your friends will have fun. We'll have a good time at the beach.

Decodable Words   Goal 8/10 Score _____ / 10

A.

sing	think	bank	keep	bean
day	stay	rain	leak	he'd

High-Frequency Words   Goal 8/10 Score _____ / 10

B.

by	car	don't	sure	ground
these	sometimes	under	your	maybe

Oral Reading Have the child read the title and the entire passage. Start timing when the child begins reading. Make an X in the text at one minute.

C.

The Beach   2

We'll bring your friends to the beach. We will   11
come by car that day. The beach is not far away.   22
It will not take long to get there.   30

We will bring food for lunch. We can put a   40
sheet on the ground. First we'll sit down and eat.   50

After lunch, we will walk around. Your friends   58
will see pink sand and clean water. They can   67
swim and play in the waves. They can put sand   77
in their pails. The main thing is to stay out of the   89
deep water.   91

Maybe they will see a bird dive for fish. The   101
fish will be the bird's lunch.   107

Your friends will have fun. We'll have a good   116
time at the beach.   120

_____ / WCPM

A.

goat	snow	we've	grow	goal
oatmeal	bread	spread	head	rowboat

B.

great	soon	paper	work	mother
more	old	try	want	door

C.

Owen's Bath Time

Owen! It is now your bath time! Go get your soap and no tricks. Fill the bathtub with water and get in. I don't want to hear moans and groans. You're going to scrub from head to feet. You know you're going to soak until you glow!

Owen! I hear something. Was it a splash? Keep the water in the bathtub. Don't splash water outside the bathtub. Don't get the rug wet. The only thing to get wet is you. You can play once you are clean.

Owen! Did you wash your face? Did you scrub your legs and feet? I am coming to see. I want to see you glow.

Decodable Words

Goal 8/10   Score _____ / 10

A.

goat	snow	we've	grow	goal
oatmeal	bread	spread	head	rowboat

High-Frequency Words

Goal 8/10   Score _____ / 10

B.

great	soon	paper	work	mother
more	old	try	want	door

Oral Reading Have the child read the title and the entire passage. Start timing when the child begins reading. Make an X in the text at one minute.

C.

Owen's Bath Time	3
Owen! It is now your bath time! Go get your	13
soap and no tricks. Fill the bathtub with water	22
and get in. I don't want to hear moans and	32
groans. You're going to scrub from head to feet.	41
You know you're going to soak until you glow!	50
Owen! I hear something. Was it a splash?	58
Keep the water in the bathtub. Don't splash	66
water outside the bathtub. Don't get the rug wet.	75
The only thing to get wet is you. You can play	86
once you are clean.	90
Owen! Did you wash your face? Did you	98
scrub your legs and feet? I am coming to see.	108
I want to see you glow.	114

_____ / WCPM

A.

bark	yarn	corn	yard	wore
cart	jars	porch	shore	fork

B.

few	loudly	night	noise	car
world	story	window	shall	more

C.

The Star Birds

I am on a baseball team called the Star Birds. My best friends are Pete and Mark. They are on the team, too.

The Star Birds play rain or shine. Our games start at four at North Park. The coach likes to start on time. Fans come to watch us play.

In our first game, I got a fly ball. It was hit hard and came at me. The fans cheered loudly. I ran fast and made the catch.

Then our team was up to bat. Pete made a run. So did Mark. I was up next and had a great hit. I made the play of the game! The Star Birds won.

Decodable Words

A.

Goal 8/10   Score _____ / 10

bark	yarn	corn	yard	wore
cart	jars	porch	shore	fork

High-Frequency Words

B.

Goal 8/10   Score _____ / 10

few	loudly	night	noise	car
world	story	window	shall	more

Oral Reading Have the child read the title and the entire passage. Start timing when the child begins reading. Make an X in the text at one minute.

C.

The Star Birds	3
I am on a baseball team called the Star	12
Birds. My best friends are Pete and Mark. They	21
are on the team, too.	26
The Star Birds play rain or shine. Our games	35
start at four at North Park. The coach likes to	45
start on time. Fans come to watch us play.	54
In our first game, I got a fly ball. It was hit	66
hard and came at me. The fans cheered loudly.	75
I ran fast and made the catch.	82
Then our team was up to bat. Pete made	91
a run. So did Mark. I was up next and had a	103
great hit. I made the play of the game! The	113
Star Birds won.	116

_____ / WCPM

A.

wood	shook	took	hook	hood
herd	dirt	fern	burn	hurt

B.

learning	young	until	follow	house
again	began	nothing	together	along

C.

Boo, the Poodle

My sister Harper and I wanted to get a dog. We read books about all kinds of dogs. Harper wanted a dog with black fur. I wanted a dog with brown fur.

Our father said maybe someday we could get a dog. He said we would have to walk it. We agreed and said we would take turns.

One night there was a noise outside. It was like a whine coming from the back door. I could hear a dog barking. Was Dad fooling us?

Just then a poodle with black and brown fur hurled into the room! She jumped into our laps, licked our faces, and wagged her tail. We adore our new dog, Boo.

Decodable Words   Goal 8/10   Score _____ / 10

A.

wood	shook	took	hook	hood
herd	dirt	fern	burn	hurt

High-Frequency Words   Goal 8/10   Score _____ / 10

B.

learning	young	until	follow	house
again	began	nothing	together	along

Oral Reading Have the child read the title and the entire passage. Start timing when the child begins reading. Make an X in the text at one minute.

C.

Boo, the Poodle	3
My sister Harper and I wanted to get a dog.	13
We read books about all kinds of dogs. Harper	22
wanted a dog with black fur. I wanted a dog with	33
brown fur.	35
Our father said maybe someday we could	42
get a dog. He said we would have to walk it. We	54
agreed and said we would take turns.	61
One night there was a noise outside. It was	70
like a whine coming from the back door. I could	80
hear a dog barking. Was Dad fooling us?	88
Just then a poodle with black and brown fur	97
hurled into the room! She jumped into our laps,	106
licked our faces, and wagged her tail. We adore	115
our new dog, Boo.	119

_____ / WCPM

A.

howl	draw	cloud	boil	cause
chew	tune	yawning	boot	blue

B.

country	ready	almost	kinds	school
buy	family	myself	please	party

C.

Owl's Clean House

Owl ran around cleaning her house. Then Owl sat down to rest. Mouse was at the door. Owl shouted, "Don't soil my house with mud." Mouse shook mud off her feet.

Skunk came by and rang the bell. "Skunk, you have mud on your paws," Owl said out loud. "Please wipe your paws on the ground now."

"Don't be such a grouch," said Skunk with a scowl. She flew in the house and left mud on the floor.

All Owl could do was frown. Mouse and Skunk cleaned up the mess. Owl was filled with joy. She was proud of her house. Owl said, "Skunk and Mouse, shall we go outside? We will visit on the lawn."

Decodable Words

Goal 8/10   Score _____ / 10

A.

howl	draw	cloud	boil	cause
chew	tune	yawning	boot	blue

High-Frequency Words

Goal 8/10   Score _____ / 10

B.

country	ready	almost	kinds	school
buy	family	myself	please	party

Oral Reading Have the child read the title and the entire passage. Start timing when the child begins reading. Make an X in the text at one minute.

C.

Owl's Clean House	3

Owl ran around cleaning her house. Then   10
Owl sat down to rest. Mouse was at the door.   20
Owl shouted, "Don't soil my house with mud."   28
Mouse shook mud off her feet.   34

Skunk came by and rang the bell. "Skunk,   42
you have mud on your paws," Owl said out loud.   52
"Please wipe your paws on the ground now."   60

"Don't be such a grouch," said Skunk with   68
a scowl. She flew in the house and tracked mud   78
on the floor.   81

All Owl could do was frown. Mouse and   89
Skunk cleaned up the mess. Owl was filled with   98
joy. She was proud of her house. Owl said,   107
"Skunk and Mouse, shall we go outside? We   115
will visit on the lawn."   120

_____ /WCPM

A.

many	cared	baby	chief	baked
dusty	field	yawning	happy	filling

B.

above	bear	even	pushed	city
toward	studied	surprised	teacher	ready

C.

The Greedy Bird

My mother and I went to the store. I got tired and hungry. I asked my mother for some money to buy a cookie. She said she was thirsty. So she bought us treats.

I got a cookie with frosting. My mother got tea with honey. We sat at a bench outside to rest and eat.

Then a bird came by us. It pecked my cookie. A piece broke off. The bird pushed the piece aside. Then the bird took the rest of my cookie. It flew away, taking the cookie with it.

I was so surprised! I shouted, "Stop that thief. It is stealing my cookie."

My mother laughed and bought me a new cookie.

Decodable Words

Goal 8/10   Score _____ / 10

A.

many	cared	baby	chief	baked
dusty	field	yawning	happy	filling

High-Frequency Words

Goal 8/10   Score _____ / 10

B.

above	bear	even	pushed	city
toward	studied	surprised	teacher	ready

Oral Reading Have the child read the title and the entire passage. Start timing when the child begins reading. Make an X in the text at one minute.

C.

The Greedy Bird

The Greedy Bird	3
My mother and I went to the store. I got	13
tired and hungry. I asked my mother for some	22
money to buy a cookie. She said she was thirsty.	32
So she bought us treats.	37
I got a cookie with frosting. My mother	45
got tea with honey. We sat at a bench outside	55
to rest and eat.	59
Then a bird came by us. It pecked my	68
cookie. A piece broke off. The bird pushed the	77
piece aside. Then the bird took the rest of my	87
cookie. It flew away, taking the cookie with it.	96
I was so surprised! I shouted, "Stop that	104
thief. It is stealing my cookie."	110
My mother laughed and bought me a	117
new cookie.	119

_____ / WCPM

A.

happiest	merrier	taller	largest	able
tie	higher	trying	cry	night

B.

always	different	happy	stories	should
across	large	heard	cried	once

C.

Be Neat When You Eat

Tonight I made a mess at the table.

Dad said, "Try to be neat when you eat. You don't want to be so messy."

What would it be like to be even messier? I might pile my sloppy food into a high hill. But then it would start to spoil and get smellier and smellier.

I might make my food fly across the table. That would be a silly sight. But it would make the table dirtier and dirtier.

"I don't think I want to be messier after all," I said.

"Let's have some apple pie," said Dad.

I was neat when I ate the pie. I was the neatest at the table!

Name _____ Date _____

Decodable Words

Goal 8/10   Score _____ / 10

A.

happiest	merrier	taller	largest	able
tie	higher	trying	cry	night

High-Frequency Words

Goal 8/10   Score _____ / 10

B.

always	different	happy	stories	should
across	large	heard	cried	once

Oral Reading Have the child read the title and the entire passage. Start timing when the child begins reading. Make an X in the text at one minute.

C.

Be Neat When You Eat	5
Tonight I made a mess at the table.	13
Dad said, "Try to be neat when you eat.	22
You don't want to be so messy."	29
What would it be like to be even messier?	38
I might pile my sloppy food into a high hill. But	49
then it would start to spoil and get smellier	58
and smellier.	60
I might make my food fly across the table.	69
That would be a silly sight. But it would make	79
the table dirtier and dirtier.	84
"I don't think I want to be messier after all,"	94
I said.	96
"Let's have some apple pie," said Dad.	103
I was neat when I ate the pie. I was the	114
neatest at the table!	118

_____ / WCPM

A.

| willful | lady | mainly | useful | lonely |
| unlike | undo | remake | untie | refill |

B.

| caught | idea | listen | beautiful | took |
| loved | most | field | everyone | people |

C.

Billy's Happy Day!

Today was a great day at school. I am so happy! I was hopeful Dad would ask me what's new. And he did!

"The teacher chose my story as the best one of the week," I replied. "I read it slowly and loudly to the whole class. Everyone clapped at the end. I was so surprised!"

"Wonderful!" Mom said. "Billy, will you please reread it to us?"

So I unpacked my backpack. I took out my story. I unfolded the paper. Then I read my story again.

Mom and Dad listened to me read. They loved my story. They told me it was likely the very best story ever. They even asked me to reread it one more time.

Decodable Words

Goal 8/10   Score _____ / 10

A.

willful	lady	mainly	useful	lonely
unlike	undo	remake	untie	refill

High-Frequency Words

Goal 8/10   Score _____ / 10

B.

caught	idea	listen	beautiful	took
loved	most	field	everyone	people

Oral Reading Have the child read the title and the entire passage. Start timing when the child begins reading. Make an X in the text at one minute.

C.

Billy's Happy Day!   3

Today was a great day at school. I am so   13
happy! I was hopeful Dad would ask me what's   22
new. And he did!   26

"The teacher chose my story as the best   34
one of the week," I replied. "I read it slowly and   45
loudly to the whole class. Everyone clapped at   53
the end. I was so surprised!"   59

"Wonderful!" Mom said. "Billy, will you   65
please reread it to us?"   70

So I unpacked my backpack. I took out my   79
story. I unfolded the paper. Then I read my   88
story again.   90

Mom and Dad listened to me read. They   98
loved my story. They told me it was likely the very   109
best story ever. They even asked me to reread it   119
one more time.   122

_____ / WCPM

Grade 2
Progress-Monitoring Assessments
Forms 1–18

Birthday Pie

Jason is glad today. It is his birthday. Five friends will come to his house to have a picnic lunch and eat snacks. Next the children will tell jokes and play games.

Jason will rip open his gifts. Will his friends bring a tent, a bug box, or a frog kit? Those were some gifts on his list. He will soon see what his friends will bring.

Will they eat birthday cake? No! Jason does not like birthday cake. Cake is too sweet. He does not like nuts or jam or plums, either. Jason likes pie.

He helps his mom sift flour until she digs in to make the crust. He licks his lips. This pie will be the best. His friends will love it.

Jason's mother will stick candles on his pie. She will turn off the lights. Then his friends and family will sit around to sing. "Happy Birthday to you!" The song will echo through the house.

Birthday Pie

2

Jason is glad today. It is his birthday. Five   11

friends will come to his house to have a picnic   21

lunch and eat snacks. Next the children will tell   30

jokes and play games.   34

Jason will rip open his gifts. Will his friends   43

bring a tent, a bug box, or a frog kit? Those were   55

some gifts on his list. He will soon see what his   66

friends will bring.   69

Will they eat birthday cake? No! Jason does   77

not like birthday cake. Cake is too sweet. He does   87

not like nuts or jam or plums, either. Jason   96

likes pie.   98

He helps his mom sift flour until she digs in   108

to make the crust. He licks his lips. This pie will be   120

the best. His friends will love it.   127

Jason's mother will stick candles on his pie.   135

She will turn off the lights. Then his friends and   145

family will sit around to sing. "Happy Birthday to   154

you!" The song will echo through the house.   162

_____ / WCPM

Bike Safety

Imagine riding your bike. It is a lot of fun! You can glide down a slope. You can pedal hard to climb a hill. Do you have good rules to follow when you ride a bike?

Do you think about what could happen? Do you judge how to stay safe? City streets are full of signs you need to read. You learn to look twice before you cross a road.

There are other rules to follow when you cycle. You should not ride too fast. This can surprise or scare other people. Ride in a line with other bikes. Slow down when others are around.

You also need to wear a bike helmet. This will help keep you safe if you fall off your bike. Your helmet should be tight on your head. You need to look at your bike, too. Is it safe to ride? Use tools to make your bike safe.

Bikes are fun to ride at any age. Just remember to keep your ride safe!

Bike Safety

2

Imagine riding your bike. It is a lot of fun!   12

You can glide down a slope. You can pedal hard   22

to climb a hill. Do you have good rules to follow   33

when you ride a bike?   38

Do you think about what could happen? Do   46

you judge how to stay safe? City streets are full   56

of signs you need to read. You learn to look twice   67

before you cross a road.   72

There are other rules to follow when you cycle.   81

You should not ride too fast. This can surprise or   91

scare other people. Ride in a line with other bikes.   101

Slow down when others are around.   107

You also need to wear a bike helmet. This will   117

help keep you safe if you fall off your bike. Your   128

helmet should be tight on your head. You need to   138

look at your bike, too. Is it safe to ride? Use tools   150

to make your bike safe.   155

Bikes are fun to ride at any age. Just   164

remember to keep your ride safe!   170

_____ / WCPM

Lily's Collection

Lily's father likes to collect clocks. Her mother has more than one hundred small, stuffed bears. Lily wants to collect things, too.

She looks in her room. Lily wonders, "What do I want to collect?" She glances at her toys. Lily does not want to collect toys. She has books. Lily does not want to collect books, either. She is not sure what to do.

Then Lily drags a box from under her bed and places it on her table. She uses the box to store her shells. Her best shells are inside it. One shell is yellow with stripes. She got it when she went to visit her friend, Clare. There is also a little, red shell. She scooped this shell from the sand after swimming at the beach.

Lily finds a third green shell that is smooth across her skin. She spotted this shell on a school trip to a lighthouse. It really shines!

Lily likes shells. She looks at them. She smiles. Now Lily knows what she will collect.

Lily's Collection

        2

     Lily's father likes to collect clocks. Her mother   10

has more than one hundred small, stuffed bears.   18

Lily wants to collect things, too.   24

     She looks in her room. Lily wonders, "What   32

do I want to collect?" She glances at her toys. Lily   43

does not want to collect toys. She has books. Lily   53

does not want to collect books, either. She is not   63

sure what to do.   67

     Then Lily drags a box from under her bed and   77

places it on her table. She uses the box to store   88

her shells. Her best shells are inside it. One shell   98

is yellow with stripes. She got it when she went   108

to visit her friend, Clare. There is also a little, red   119

shell. She scooped this shell from the sand after   128

swimming at the beach.   132

     Lily finds a third green shell that is smooth   141

across her skin. She spotted this shell on a school   151

trip to a lighthouse. It really shines!   158

     Lily likes shells. She looks at them. She smiles.   167

Now Lily knows what she will collect.   174

_____ / WCPM

Amazing Earthworms

Most people ignore the earthworm. It is often hidden under the ground. Did you know that earthworms are good for gardens?

They dig in the ground by eating and pushing the soil. They make burrows, or tunnels. Their work breaks up the soil and makes stiff ground soft. The soft ground helps plants grow. Roots can spread. Stems can find their way to the air. The more earthworms you have, the better your garden will be.

Earthworms need to stay wet to live. They must have the right kind of climate. They do not appear above ground during the day, unless it rains. The Sun might dry them up. Earthworms come out at night to track down food to eat. Then they wiggle back into the ground. This is where they want to be.

Some soil is full of earthworms. Some is not. People buy earthworms to add to their gardens. This makes earthworms and people very happy.

Name _____ Date _____

Amazing Earthworms

2

Most people ignore the earthworm. It is often   10

hidden under the ground. Did you know that   18

earthworms are good for gardens?   23

They dig in the ground by eating and pushing   32

the soil. They make burrows, or tunnels. Their   40

work breaks up the soil and makes stiff ground   49

soft. The soft ground helps plants grow. Roots   57

can spread. Stems can find their way to the air.   67

The more earthworms you have, the better your   75

garden will be.   78

Earthworms need to stay wet to live. They   86

must have the right kind of climate. They do not   96

appear above ground during the day, unless it   104

rains. The Sun might dry them up. Earthworms   112

come out at night to track down food to eat. Then   123

they wiggle back into the ground. This is where   132

they want to be.   136

Some soil is full of earthworms. Some is not.   145

People buy earthworms to add to their gardens.   153

This makes earthworms and people very happy.   160

_____ / WCPM

At the Beach

Ben and his family walked on the beach. Ben liked the beach and the sunshine. He hopped in the sand. It was rough with pebbles, but he kept hopping.

Ben spotted fish in a narrow bit of water. They were swimming close together. His father snapped a photo. Then Ben watched two crabs hiding near some shells. He wondered which shell the bigger crab would decide to live in. He also saw a few birds flying high in the sky. Would they catch some fish to eat?

Many people were swimming and splashing in the water. A dog chased a yellow ball. Ben saw children making sandcastles. What would it be like to join them later? They were having a lot of fun.

He sat near some children on the beach and watched. Then he helped to make the sandcastle. Ben had a happy day at the beach!

Progress-Monitoring Assessments
SESSIONS 2.9A, 2.9B, 2.9C, 2.10A, 2.10B, 2.10C

At the Beach

Ben and his family walked on the beach. Ben   12
liked the beach and the sunshine. He hopped in   21
the sand. It was rough with pebbles, but he kept   31
hopping.   32

Ben spotted fish in a narrow bit of water.   41
They were swimming close together. His father   48
snapped a photo. Then Ben watched two crabs   56
hiding near some shells. He wondered which   63
shell the bigger crab would decide to live in. He   73
also saw a few birds flying high in the sky. Would   84
they catch some fish to eat?   90

Many people were swimming and splashing in   97
the water. A dog chased a yellow ball. Ben saw   107
children making sandcastles. What would it be   114
like to join them later? They were having a lot   124
of fun.   126

He sat near some children on the beach and   135
watched. Then he helped to make the sandcastle.   143
Ben had a happy day at the beach!   151

3

_____ / WCPM

Bumblebees

A bee is made up of different parts. Each part has a special use. Let's look at how a bee uses three of these parts.

A bee has five eyes. Two eyes are large, and three eyes are small. A bee's eyes can see things move. They see different colors than we do. For example, a bee can't see red!

A bee flies with four wings. It must move its wings fast to fly. If it doesn't, it won't lift up in the air. Bees fly from flower to flower. They are looking for pollen. This helps flowers grow.

A bee has six legs. Some of its legs have hair on them. The hair helps carry the pollen bees find.

Do you feel nervous around bees? Many people become tense around bees. We've heard that they sometimes can sting. We're afraid we'll get hurt. But if we leave bees alone, they'll leave us alone, too!

Bumblebees

       1

    A bee is made up of different parts. Each   10

part has a special use. Let's look at how a bee   21

uses three of these parts.   26

    A bee has five eyes. Two eyes are large, and   36

three eyes are small. A bee's eyes can see things   46

move. They see different colors than we do. For   55

example, a bee can't see red!   61

    A bee flies with four wings. It must move its   71

wings fast to fly. If it doesn't, it won't lift up in   83

the air. Bees fly from flower to flower. They are   93

looking for pollen. This helps flowers grow.   100

    A bee has six legs. Some of its legs have hair   111

on them. The hair helps carry the pollen bees find.   121

    Do you feel nervous around bees? Many   128

people become tense around bees. We've heard   135

that they sometimes can sting. We're afraid we'll   143

get hurt. But if we leave bees alone, they'll leave   153

us alone, too!   156

_____ / WCPM

Tom Saves the Day

Tom talks to his friends about his new job. Tom used to sit at a gray desk all day. He missed being outside in the fresh air and sunlight. He wanted something different.

Now his job is much more fun! He works on a fishing boat. "I like how the boat sways in the wind when we put up the sail!" says Tom. "I like the way the water sprays over the rails."

Tom tells a story. He was on the boat, far out in the bay. He saw a large fish through the misty rain. It was caught in bunches of fishing line. The fish fought but could not get out! The water was not deep enough, and the fish would die soon.

"We pulled the boat up and stayed close to the fish," says Tom. "I heard its tail flapping against the water." Tom was afraid he would not free the fish in time.

Then he raised the line, and the fish twisted out! "I saved the fish!" Tom loves his new job.

Progress-Monitoring Assessments
SESSIONS 2.13A, 2.13B, 2.14A, 2.14B

Tom Saves the Day

Tom talks to his friends about his new job.   13

Tom used to sit at a gray desk all day. He missed   25

being outside in the fresh air and sunlight. He   34

wanted something different.   37

     Now his job is much more fun! He works on   47

a fishing boat. "I like how the boat sways in the   58

wind when we put up the sail!" says Tom. "I like   69

the way the water sprays over the rails."   77

     Tom tells a story. He was on the boat, far out   88

in the bay. He saw a large fish through the misty   99

rain. It was caught in bunches of fishing line. The   109

fish fought but could not get out! The water was   119

not deep enough, and the fish would die soon.   128

     "We pulled the boat up and stayed close   136

to the fish," says Tom. "I heard its tail flapping   146

against the water." Tom was afraid he would not   155

free the fish in time.   160

     Then he raised the line, and the fish twisted   169

out! "I saved the fish!" Tom loves his new job.   179

_____ / WCPM

Dinosaur Museum

Welcome to the museum. It is open all week, and Mondays are free. We have space to keep your coats as you get started.

If you like, a person who works here can lead you through and show you different things from around the world. You may also walk through the museum with only your family.

Do you dream of seeing dinosaurs? This museum has the bones of many different kinds! You will see models of baby dinosaurs. You will even see real dinosaur eggs that were found in the ground.

Everyone needs to follow a few rules at the museum. Please walk slowly. Never run. Do not bring in food and drinks. Eat meals only in the food areas. You must stay with your leader, even if you want to peek at something else. Objects are old and break easily, so do not touch things in the museum. Be very careful!

Have fun while you visit. It is a pleasure to have you here!

Dinosaur Museum

Welcome to the museum. It is open all week,	11
and Mondays are free. We have space to keep	20
your coats as you get started.	26
If you like, a person who works here can lead	36
you through and show you different things from	44
around the world. You may also walk through the	53
museum with only your family.	58
Do you dream of seeing dinosaurs? This	65
museum has the bones of many different kinds!	73
You will see models of baby dinosaurs. You will	82
even see real dinosaur eggs that were found in	91
the ground.	93
Everyone needs to follow a few rules at the	102
museum. Please walk slowly. Never run. Do not	110
bring in food and drinks. Eat meals only in the	120
food areas. You must stay with your leader, even	129
if you want to peek at something else. Objects	138
are old and break easily, so do not touch things in	149
the museum. Be very careful!	154
Have fun while you visit. It is a pleasure to	164
have you here!	167

_____ / WCPM

Digging for Clams

Have you ever found seashells on the beach? Many shells are clamshells. Clams often live underwater in the wet sand or mud.

A clam's shell has two parts. The parts open and close like a mouth. The clam opens its shell to get food. An open clam can look ready to bite down. Does anybody trust a hungry mouth?

Have you ever thought about digging for clams? It is not always fun. Clams can be hard to find. They like to stay hidden. Maybe they know they are good to eat!

There is a lot of mud when you dig for clams. People might wear boots or raincoats to keep from getting muddy. Then it can be fun to pluck one from the mud.

There are many ways to cook clams. You can find recipes in a book. Does digging for clams sound too hard? There is an easier way to get them. You can buy clams at a fish shop or a grocery store, too!

Digging for Clams

Have you ever found seashells on the beach? 3 11

Many shells are clamshells. Clams often live 18

underwater in the wet sand or mud. 25

A clam's shell has two parts. The parts open 34

and close like a mouth. The clam opens its shell 44

to get food. An open clam can look ready to bite 55

down. Does anybody trust a hungry mouth? 62

Have you ever thought about digging for 69

clams? It is not always fun. Clams can be hard to 80

find. They like to stay hidden. Maybe they know 89

they are good to eat! 94

There is a lot of mud when you dig for clams. 105

People might wear boots or raincoats to keep 113

from getting muddy. Then it can be fun to pluck 123

one from the mud. 127

There are many ways to cook clams. You can 136

find recipes in a book. Does digging for clams 145

sound too hard? There is an easier way to get 155

them. You can buy clams at a fish shop or a 166

grocery store, too! 169

_____ / WCPM

Dr. Seuss

Do you know the name Dr. Seuss? That might be because you have read his books. Maybe your teacher has his books in the classroom right now! Dr. Seuss was a writer of many children's books. Children like his funny pictures and rhymes.

Dr. Seuss was born in 1904. In school, he liked to write stories with funny pictures. He also decided to try designing cartoons. He wanted to see whether he was good at it. He was!

When Dr. Seuss finished and sold his first cartoon, he moved to New York City. He wrote his first story in 1937.

Twenty years later, he wrote *The Cat in the Hat*. In this story, two children wonder why the Sun does not shine. They are surprised at the sight of the wild cat that stops by! It is very funny. Many more stories delighted readers before Dr. Seuss died in 1991.

Today children still love his books. There is something in his stories for any age. Do you have a Dr. Seuss book that you love?

Dr. Seuss

Do you know the name Dr. Seuss? That might 11

be because you have read his books. Maybe your 20

teacher has his books in the classroom right now! 29

Dr. Seuss was a writer of many children's books. 38

Children like his funny pictures and rhymes. 45

Dr. Seuss was born in 1904. In school, he 54

liked to write stories with funny pictures. He also 63

decided to try designing cartoons. He wanted to 71

see whether he was good at it. He was! 80

When Dr. Seuss finished and sold his first 88

cartoon, he moved to New York City. He wrote his 98

first story in 1937. 102

Twenty years later, he wrote *The Cat in the* 111

Hat. In this story, two children wonder why the 120

Sun does not shine. They are surprised at the 129

sight of the wild cat that stops by! It is very funny. 141

Many more stories delighted readers before 147

Dr. Seuss died in 1991. 152

Today children still love his books. There is 160

something in his stories for any age. Do you have 170

a Dr. Seuss book that you love? 177

_____ / WCPM

A Good Day

I was working at my desk when my teacher walked up to me. Was he going to warn me to study harder? No, he was smiling.

"Amy, I have great news," he said. "Your drawing of the lizard won first prize in our contest. We would like to hang it at school for the March Art Fair."

As he passed me two copies of the award certificate, my friends clapped loudly. I gripped the copies in shaky hands. I could not believe I won first prize!

The bell rang, and I tossed my books into my empty bag. I could hardly wait to tell my family the happy news. I ran home quickly! As soon as I opened the door, I shouted to my mother, "I got first prize! My drawing will be hanging in a fancy frame."

My mother smiled. "Ever since you were a baby, you've always loved to draw. I am very proud of you!"

She reminded me that all my hours of practice had been worthwhile. It was a good day.

Progress-Monitoring Assessments
SESSIONS 2.21A, 2.21B,
2.21C, 2.22A, 2.22B

A Good Day

3

I was working at my desk when my teacher 12

walked up to me. Was he going to warn me to 23

study harder? No, he was smiling. 29

"Amy, I have great news," he said. "Your 37

drawing of the lizard won first prize in our 46

contest. We would like to hang it at school for the 57

March Art Fair." 60

As he passed me two copies of the award 69

certificate, my friends clapped loudly. I gripped 76

the copies in shaky hands. I could not believe 85

I won first prize! 89

The bell rang, and I tossed my books into my 99

empty bag. I could hardly wait to tell my family 109

the happy news. I ran home quickly! As soon as I 120

opened the door, I shouted to my mother, "I got 130

first prize! My drawing will be hanging in a fancy 140

frame." 141

My mother smiled. "Ever since you were a 149

baby, you've always loved to draw. I am very 158

proud of you!" 161

She reminded me that all my hours of practice 170

had been worthwhile. It was a good day. 178

_____ / WCPM

The King of Insects

Could the beetle be the king of insects? There are almost 400,000 kinds of beetles on Earth. That is more beetles than any other kind of insect.

Have you ever explored the ground for bugs? Have you searched your own back porch? Be ready to find beetles in many colors. They can be brown or black. They can be red or green and more. Beetles also come in different sizes and forms. The biggest are six inches long.

Ladybugs are a very pretty kind of beetle. You may have held a ladybug in your hand. People with gardens buy boxes of ladybugs from a store. The ladybugs eat insects that chew or bore into garden plants and often destroy them. This helps the garden plants grow.

Some people keep beetles as pets. Some people eat beetles. Imagine sorting all the animals in the world in a single line. Every fourth one would be a beetle.

That is a lot of beetles! This is why the beetle is called the king of insects.

The King of Insects

    Could the beetle be the king of insects? There   **13**

are almost 400,000 kinds of beetles on Earth.   **21**

That is more beetles than any other kind of insect.   **31**

Have you ever explored the ground for bugs?   **39**

Have you searched your own back porch? Be   **47**

ready to find beetles in many colors. They can be   **57**

brown or black. They can be red or green and   **67**

more. Beetles also come in different sizes and   **75**

forms. The biggest are six inches long.   **82**

    Ladybugs are a very pretty kind of beetle. You   **91**

may have held a ladybug in your hand. People   **100**

with gardens buy boxes of ladybugs from a store.   **109**

The ladybugs eat insects that chew or bore into   **118**

garden plants and often destroy them. This helps   **126**

the garden plants grow.   **130**

    Some people keep beetles as pets. Some   **137**

people eat beetles. Imagine sorting all the   **144**

animals in the world in a single line. Every fourth   **154**

one would be a beetle.   **159**

    That is a lot of beetles! This is why the beetle   **170**

is called the king of insects.   **176**

_____ / WCPM

The Park

Where do you like to go in winter? Our park is glorious when the weather turns cold. The pond freezes, making a perfect place to ice skate. It is thrilling to twirl on the ice!

When it snows, everyone brings a colorful sled. Children curl up on their sleds and swerve quickly down the hill. There are three hills in the park. The third has the deepest snow. Be sure to be very careful where the bigger trees line the hill. You do not want to hit one!

What's another sight at the park? You might see squirrels and birds. Here's a red bird flying in a burst of color across the sea of snow.

What sounds might you hear? When the snow falls, the park becomes quiet. Listen and you might hear a woodpecker pecking the older trees. It is looking for bugs to eat.

An hour passes quickly in our park. Remember to wear your hat and boots to stay warm. One visit and you will surely return!

The Park

Where do you like to go in winter? Our park   12

is glorious when the weather turns cold. The pond   21

freezes, making a perfect place to ice skate. It is   31

thrilling to twirl on the ice!   37

When it snows, everyone brings a colorful   44

sled. Children curl up on their sleds and swerve   53

quickly down the hill. There are three hills in the   63

park. The third has the deepest snow. Be sure to   73

be very careful where the bigger trees line the hill.   83

You do not want to hit one!   90

What's another sight at the park? You might   98

see squirrels and birds. Here's a red bird flying in   108

a burst of color across the sea of snow.   117

What sounds might you hear? When the   124

snow falls, the park becomes quiet. Listen and   132

you might hear a woodpecker pecking the older   140

trees. It is looking for bugs to eat.   148

An hour passes quickly in our park.   155

Remember to wear your hat and boots to stay   164

warm. One visit and you will surely return!   172

_____ / WCPM

A Silly Day

"Tomorrow is Wear Something Silly Day at school," Sara told her mother. "I want to wear something silly, but I don't know what to wear."

Sara's mother asked her whether she had any clothes that looked silly. Sara shook her head sadly. Her mother told her to look in her bedroom closet and in the brown trunk in the attic. Sara went to her closet and looked closely at all of the clothes there. Then she went up to the attic. She got down on her knees and carefully looked through the trunk. None of the clothes were silly, so she repacked them. As she was coming down the stairs, she had an idea.

"I might have a solution," she told her mother. Sara went back into her room and picked out some clothes. She turned the clothes inside out and then put them on backward. Then she showed her mother. "Here I am, Mom. What do you think?" she asked.

"That's a very silly outfit!" her mother said. "What a great idea!" Sara agreed.

Progress-Monitoring Assessments
SESSIONS 2.27A, 2.27B, 2.27C, 2.28A, 2.28B, 2.28C

A Silly Day

"Tomorrow is Wear Something Silly Day at 10
school," Sara told her mother. "I want to wear 19
something silly, but I don't know what to wear." 28

Sara's mother asked her whether she 34
had any clothes that looked silly. Sara shook her 43
head sadly. Her mother told her to look in 52
her bedroom closet and in the brown trunk in the 62
attic. Sara went to her closet and looked closely 71
at all of the clothes there. Then she went up to 82
the attic. She got down on her knees and carefully 92
looked through the trunk. None of the clothes 100
were silly, so she repacked them. As she was 109
coming down the stairs, she had an idea. 117

"I might have a solution," she told her 125
mother. Sara went back into her room and picked 134
out some clothes. She turned the clothes inside 142
out and then put them on backward. Then she 151
showed her mother. "Here I am, Mom. What do 160
you think?" she asked. 164

"That's a very silly outfit!" her mother said. 172
"What a great idea!" Sara agreed. 178

_____ / WCPM

Space Story

Hona was at her computer. Three moons shone through her window. She checked her report to make sure all of the words were spelled correctly. She caught one misspelled word and corrected it.

Once she was done with her report, Hona searched the computer for other things she wanted to learn. She saw an article called "Global Warming Could Prove Fatal." It was about a planet very far away. Hona had never even heard of the planet. It was called Earth.

She called out, "Father! You have to hear this. There's a planet in the Milky Way system that's still using oil for energy! Come see!"

Mr. Mercury entered his daughter's room and read the article. "This is interesting! They're close enough to their Sun to use its energy! They have wind and ocean waves, too. Why aren't they using those energies for power?"

Hona concluded, "I think we should take a spaceship and go over there to talk to them about other things they can do."

**Progress-Monitoring
Assessments**
SESSIONS 2.29A,
2.29B, 2.30

Space Story

2

Hona was at her computer. Three moons 9

shone through her window. She checked her 16

report to make sure all of the words were spelled 26

correctly. She caught one misspelled word and 33

corrected it. 35

Once she was done with her report, Hona 43

searched the computer for other things she 50

wanted to learn. She saw an article called "Global 59

Warming Could Prove Fatal." It was about a 67

planet very far away. Hona had never even heard 76

of the planet. It was called Earth. 83

She called out, "Father! You have to hear this. 92

There's a planet in the Milky Way system that's still 102

using oil for energy! Come see!" 108

Mr. Mercury entered his daughter's room and 115

read the article. "This is interesting! They're close 123

enough to their Sun to use its energy! They have 133

wind and ocean waves, too. Why aren't they using 142

those energies for power?" 146

Hona concluded, "I think we should take a 154

spaceship and go over there to talk to them about 164

other things they can do." 169

_____ / WCPM

Ramona and Ben

It was such a beautiful day that Ramona had a yearning to be outside. She called out, "Where are you, Ben? Do you want to go to the park?"

Ben flew into the room and said, "I love the park. I'm always ready for an adventure. I wish we could go to the park every day. Today is going to be a wonderful day!" He put on his collar. "I can hardly wait to splash in the brook and push you on the wooden swing." Ben ran to get a few things to take to the park. He got his football and a good book to read.

"Ben, you don't need all that!" Ramona exclaimed as she shook her head in wonder.

"Yes, I do, I truly do!" Ben answered firmly as he refused to put them back.

Ramona knew it was useless to argue, so she took Ben's leash off its hook and said, "Are we ready now?"

Ben wiggled with excitement and followed Ramona out the door. He knew it would be a memorable day.

Ramona and Ben

It was such a beautiful day that Ramona had   12

a yearning to be outside. She called out, "Where   21

are you, Ben? Do you want to go to the park?"   32

Ben flew into the room and said, "I love the   42

park. I'm always ready for an adventure. I wish   52

we could go to the park every day. Today is going   63

to be a wonderful day!" He put on his collar. "I   73

can hardly wait to splash in the brook and push   83

you on the wooden swing." Ben ran to get a few   94

things to take to the park. He got his football and   105

a good book to read.   110

"Ben, you don't need all that!" Ramona   117

exclaimed as she shook her head in wonder.   125

"Yes, I do, I truly do!" Ben answered firmly as   135

he refused to put them back.   141

Ramona knew it was useless to argue, so she   150

took Ben's leash off its hook and said, "Are we   160

ready now?"   162

Ben wiggled with excitement and followed   168

Ramona out the door. He knew it would be a   178

memorable day.   180

_____ / WCPM

Mike's Idea

Mike's class wanted to do something special for the children at the hospital. The class decided to raise money to buy books. The students would have a cookie sale at school. When he got home, Mike asked his mother for help making cookies. She said, "I am sorry, but I have too much to do today."

Mike asked his father for help. He said, "I am sorry. I would enjoy making cookies, but I promised to help your sister paint her toy chest."

"Who else could I ask?" Mike thought. Then Mike devised a plan. He called his pal Tran, who lived nearby. They could make cookies together! Tran asked his grandfather. His grandfather replied, "I loved baking cookies during my boyhood. I would be delighted to help you both."

Mike took sugar and flour to Tran's house. Mike, Tran, and Tran's grandfather baked cookies. The next day, the boys sold cookies. They used the money to buy seven books for the children at the hospital. Next time they hope to raise enough money for even more books.

Progress-Monitoring Assessments
SESSIONS 2.33A, 2.33B,
2.34A, 2.34B, 2.34C

Mike's Idea

2

Mike's class wanted to do something special · 9

for the children at the hospital. The class decided · 18

to raise money to buy books. The students would · 27

have a cookie sale at school. When he got home, · 37

Mike asked his mother for help making cookies. · 45

She said, "I am sorry, but I have too much to do · 57

today." · 58

Mike asked his father for help. He said, "I · 67

am sorry. I would enjoy making cookies, but I · 76

promised to help your sister paint her toy chest." · 85

"Who else could I ask?" Mike thought. Then · 93

Mike devised a plan. He called his pal Tran, who · 103

lived nearby. They could make cookies together! · 110

Tran asked his grandfather. His grandfather · 116

replied, "I loved baking cookies during my · 123

boyhood. I would be delighted to help you both." · 132

Mike took sugar and flour to Tran's house. · 140

Mike, Tran, and Tran's grandfather baked cookies. · 147

The next day, the boys sold cookies. They used · 156

the money to buy seven books for the children at · 166

the hospital. Next time they hope to raise enough · 175

money for even more books. · 180

_____ / WCPM

Wanda's Swamp

Wanda likes to visit the swamp. A swamp is a place that is very wet. Wanda's dad takes her around the swamp in his boat. They float under the big willow trees and gum trees.

Many animals live in the swamp. Wanda stays alert in the boat. She looks out for cottonmouth snakes. She knows they are very dangerous. Wanda's dad likes to watch for birds. He points out the different birds in the sky. Many are social birds and stay together in groups. There are many animals in the swamp that they never see. The bobcat stays away from people. Fish swim below in the water, but the water is too dark to see them.

From the boat, Wanda can see a turtle. It sleeps on a sunny spot on a rock. She watches a beetle take a dive. Two years ago, Wanda saw a raccoon catching a fish. But the most exciting day at the swamp that she can remember was when she saw two bear cubs running between the trees!

Name ______________________ Date __________

Wanda's Swamp 2

Wanda likes to visit the swamp. A swamp is 11
a place that is very wet. Wanda's dad takes her 21
around the swamp in his boat. They float under 30
the big willow trees and gum trees. 37

Many animals live in the swamp. Wanda stays 45
alert in the boat. She looks out for cottonmouth 54
snakes. She knows they are very dangerous. 61
Wanda's dad likes to watch for birds. He points 70
out the different birds in the sky. Many are social 80
birds and stay together in groups. There are many 89
animals in the swamp that they never see. The 98
bobcat stays away from people. Fish swim below 106
in the water, but the water is too dark to see 117
them. 118

From the boat, Wanda can see a turtle. It 127
sleeps on a sunny spot on a rock. She watches a 138
beetle take a dive. Two years ago, Wanda saw a 148
raccoon catching a fish. But the most exciting day 157
at the swamp that she can remember was when 166
she saw two bear cubs running between the trees! 175

______ / WCPM

Grade 3

Progress-Monitoring Assessments

Forms 1–18

Going Fishing

One sunny afternoon, Sam and his grandfather went fishing. They walked through the woods to the edge of the lake. Sam found a log for them to sit on. His grandfather set up their poles. Then they put worms on the hooks. While they sat on the log fishing, Sam's grandfather told interesting stories.

Soon Sam had a bite on his line. He reeled the line in and caught his first fish. Sam was so excited that he almost fell into the water. His grandfather helped him get the fish off the hook and put it in the bucket promptly. Together they sat talking and fishing until huge black clouds blocked the Sun.

"Uh-oh, looks like a storm is coming," said Sam's grandfather. He was about to suggest they leave when thunder rumbled in the distance. Rain was falling across the lake.

They packed their things. As they walked back through the woods, the rain began to pour down. "This looks serious!" said Sam's grandfather.

When they got to the car, they were soaking wet. Sam was cold, but he was happy. He could appreciate the time he spent fishing, even though it was short.

Going Fishing

	2

One sunny afternoon, Sam and his grandfather   9

went fishing. They walked through the woods to the   18

edge of the lake. Sam found a log for them to sit on.   31

His grandfather set up their poles. Then they put   40

worms on the hooks. While they sat on the log fishing,   51

Sam's grandfather told interesting stories.   56

Soon Sam had a bite on his line. He reeled the line   68

in and caught his first fish. Sam was so excited that   79

he almost fell into the water. His grandfather helped   88

him get the fish off the hook and put it in the bucket   101

promptly. Together they sat talking and fishing until   109

huge black clouds blocked the Sun.   115

"Uh-oh, looks like a storm is coming," said Sam's   124

grandfather. He was about to suggest they leave when   133

thunder rumbled in the distance. Rain was falling across   142

the lake.   144

They packed their things. As they walked back   152

through the woods, the rain began to pour down. "This   162

looks serious!" said Sam's grandfather.   167

When they got to the car, they were soaking wet.   177

Sam was cold, but he was happy. He could appreciate   187

the time he spent fishing, even though it was short.   197

_____ / WCPM

A Thanksgiving to Remember

There is one Thanksgiving on the farm that I remember quite fondly. It had been an extremely long, hot summer. Then came the drought. If memory serves, it didn't rain for a month straight. Next the locusts arrived. They were ferocious, eating all plants in their path. And the war raged on, which added to the gloom.

We had a cow, so there was plenty of milk available. Mom thinned the mashed potatoes by adding butter and cream. Some neighbors brought us a small chicken that served as a "turkey," and the cabbage had to do as a green vegetable.

We all appeared glum when dinner was ready. Just as we sat down, there was a knock on the door. I answered it. There stood my brother, Matt, handsome as a prince in his army uniform. I screamed and jumped into his arms. My shriek was followed by shouts of joy. Soon everyone was squealing with excitement that Matt had been released from the army.

Sometimes I mash my potatoes just like we did that Thanksgiving. I add so much butter and cream that they hardly pile up at all. It brings the memory back.

A Thanksgiving to Remember

There is one Thanksgiving on the farm that I	4
	13

There is one Thanksgiving on the farm that I   13

remember quite fondly. It had been an extremely   21

long, hot summer. Then came the drought. If memory   30

serves, it didn't rain for a month straight. Next the   40

locusts arrived. They were ferocious, eating all plants   48

in their path. And the war raged on, which added to   59

the gloom.   61

We had a cow, so there was plenty of milk   71

available. Mom thinned the mashed potatoes by adding   79

butter and cream. Some neighbors brought us a small   88

chicken that served as a "turkey," and the cabbage   97

had to do as a green vegetable.   104

We all appeared glum when dinner was ready.   112

Just as we sat down, there was a knock on the door.   124

I answered it. There stood my brother, Matt, handsome   133

as a prince in his army uniform. I screamed and jumped   144

into his arms. My shriek was followed by shouts of joy.   155

Soon everyone was squealing with excitement that   162

Matt had been released from the army.   169

Sometimes I mash my potatoes just like we did that   179

Thanksgiving. I add so much butter and cream that   188

they hardly pile up at all. It brings the memory back.   199

_____ / WCPM

The Land of the Midnight Sun

Iceland is a country that is also a large island. It is a great place to see. It is very far north in the North Atlantic Ocean. In the winter, it is very dark. There is daylight for only four to six hours a day. But for about three months in summer, it doesn't get dark at all. That is why some people call Iceland "the land of the midnight Sun."

Even though Iceland is very far north, it is not as cold as you might think. Most people in Iceland live near the sea. Warm winds from the sea help to keep the land from getting very cold. The summers in Iceland are cool, too. It feels more like spring than the hot summers we are used to in the United States. Iceland is a wonderful place to visit. It is very pretty, and many animals live there, including foxes, rabbits, and reindeer. You should think about going to see this island soon!

The Land of the Midnight Sun

The Land of the Midnight Sun	6
Iceland is a country that is also a large island. It	17
is a great place to see. It is very far north in the North	31
Atlantic Ocean. In the winter, it is very dark. There is	42
daylight for only four to six hours a day. But for about	54
three months in summer, it doesn't get dark at all.	64
That is why some people call Iceland "the land of the	75
midnight Sun."	77
Even though Iceland is very far north, it is not	87
as cold as you might think. Most people in Iceland	97
live near the sea. Warm winds from the sea help to	108
keep the land from getting very cold. The summers	117
in Iceland are cool, too. It feels more like spring than	128
the hot summers we are used to in the United States.	139
Iceland is a wonderful place to visit. It is very pretty,	150
and many animals live there, including foxes, rabbits,	158
and reindeer. You should think about going to see this	168
island soon!	170

_____ / WCPM

The Quick Save

Robert floated lazily on his back and thought how good it felt to gaze at the perfectly blue sky as the afternoon sun warmed his skin. He let the gentle ocean waves push him toward the shore, just a few yards away, where swimmers splashed in the surf.

Suddenly, a shout interrupted his thoughts. He tried to ignore it, but the panic in the voice made this impossible. "Help, please help! Somebody help her!" a woman frantically screamed.

"She needs help!" someone yelled. At first Robert's brain wouldn't function, so he couldn't tell what was happening. As his toes touched the sand, he heard his sister Anna's urgent voice. "She's over there, Robert! Get her!" Anna was pointing to the waves nearby.

Looking around quickly, Robert watched as a child struggled to keep her head above water. Without another thought, he dove and reached for her. His fingers soon closed around a tiny arm. Grasping the girl with strong hands, Robert lifted her out of the water. His only thought now was for her safety. She coughed and then began to cry. With relief, Robert knew this meant she would be all right.

The Quick Save

   3

Robert floated lazily on his back and thought how   12

good it felt to gaze at the perfectly blue sky as the   24

afternoon sun warmed his skin. He let the gentle ocean   34

waves push him toward the shore, just a few yards   44

away, where swimmers splashed in the surf.   51

    Suddenly, a shout interrupted his thoughts. He   58

tried to ignore it, but the panic in the voice made this   70

impossible. "Help, please help! Somebody help her!"   77

a woman frantically screamed.   81

    "She needs help!" someone yelled. At first   88

Robert's brain wouldn't function, so he couldn't tell   96

what was happening. As his toes touched the sand,   105

he heard his sister Anna's urgent voice. "She's over   114

there, Robert! Get her!" Anna was pointing to the   123

waves nearby.   125

    Looking around quickly, Robert watched as a child   133

struggled to keep her head above water. Without   141

another thought, he dove and reached for her. His   150

fingers soon closed around a tiny arm. Grasping the girl   160

with strong hands, Robert lifted her out of the water.   170

His only thought now was for her safety. She coughed   180

and then began to cry. With relief, Robert knew this   190

meant she would be all right.   196

_____ / WCPM

Jenny's Game

Jenny was excited to become a member of the baseball team. Most of the team hadn't wanted a girl to join. But her cousin Roger was an influential member of the team. He knew that she was a great pitcher. So he convinced the coach that her skill would help them win games. His teammates still had their doubts.

Tonight after six innings, the team was behind. Roger urged the coach to let Jenny pitch. "What will the other team think if we send a girl out to pitch?" Jenny heard one player ask.

Jenny replied, "What will they think if I strike them out?"

"Give her a try!" another player called. Curiosity was rising. The boys wanted to see what she would do. Jenny wanted to show that they were wrong to think a girl couldn't pitch.

When Jenny walked up to the pitcher's mound, there were jeers from her foes on the other team. She bounced on her feet and then blew on her knuckles. Then she braced her knees, twisted her wrist, and threw her own special pitch. When Jenny struck out the third player, her teammates cheered as she walked back to the dugout.

Jenny's Game

Jenny was excited to become a member of the baseball team. Most of the team hadn't wanted a girl to join. But her cousin Roger was an influential member of the team. He knew that she was a great pitcher. So he convinced the coach that her skill would help them win games. His teammates still had their doubts.

Tonight after six innings, the team was behind. Roger urged the coach to let Jenny pitch. "What will the other team think if we send a girl out to pitch?" Jenny heard one player ask.

Jenny replied, "What will they think if I strike them out?"

"Give her a try!" another player called. Curiosity was rising. The boys wanted to see what she would do. Jenny wanted to show that they were wrong to think a girl couldn't pitch.

When Jenny walked up to the pitcher's mound, there were jeers from her foes on the other team. She bounced on her feet and then blew on her knuckles. Then she braced her knees, twisted her wrist, and threw her own special pitch. When Jenny struck out the third player, her teammates cheered as she walked back to the dugout.

_____ / WCPM

Symbols of Freedom

How many kinds of eagles do you think live in the world? If you guessed about sixty, you would be right. Some kinds of eagles are large. Some kinds are small. Most are strong for their size. Some are even strong enough to lift food that is almost as heavy as they are!

Eagles have been used as symbols of freedom in the United States. Some people call them the "king of birds." This is because of their brave, proud looks. In 1782, the United States officially chose the bald eagle to be on its Great Seal. From that point on, the bald eagle has been recognized as the national bird of the United States. The bald eagle has had a great amount of publicity since then.

Bald eagles are large birds. They can weigh from eight to thirteen pounds. Some eagles have wings that spread as much as seven feet across! Their heads are covered with white feathers. The bald eagle is a very good choice for our national bird.

Symbols of Freedom
3

How many kinds of eagles do you think live in the   14

world? If you guessed about sixty, you would be right.   24

Some kinds of eagles are large. Some kinds are small.   34

Most are strong for their size. Some are even strong   44

enough to lift food that is almost as heavy as they are!   56

Eagles have been used as symbols of freedom in   65

the United States. Some people call them the "king of   75

birds." This is because of their brave, proud looks. In   85

1782, the United States officially chose the bald eagle   94

to be on its Great Seal. From that point on, the bald   106

eagle has been recognized as the national bird of the   116

United States. The bald eagle has had a great amount   126

of publicity since then.   130

Bald eagles are large birds. They can weigh from   139

eight to thirteen pounds. Some eagles have wings that   148

spread as much as seven feet across! Their heads are   158

covered with white feathers. The bald eagle is a very   168

good choice for our national bird.   174

_____ / WCPM

Mr. Clark's Class

Mr. Clark's class was excited today. Pets were allowed in school today! The children had brought puppies, cats, and a rabbit. There were also a lizard, a snake, two hamsters, a turtle, and even a chicken. Each boy and girl wrote a story about his or her pet and read it aloud.

Soon it was lunchtime. The children left the animals in the classroom. As soon as the door was closed, the animals started to create turmoil. The puppies chased the cats down an aisle. The hamsters and turtle began eating the children's work. One puppy tried to bury a pencil. The rabbit knocked over some paint, and the paint spilled onto the lizard. The snake crawled into Mr. Clark's desk, and the chicken deliberately laid an egg on top of it!

When the class got back from lunch, the children saw what the pets had done. Quickly they began cleaning up the mess. Just as they finished, Mr. Clark walked back in. He pointed at the quiet animals and said, "I am really enjoying today. We can all take a lesson from your pets and be so well behaved."

Mr. Clark's Class

Mr. Clark's class was excited today. Pets were	11

Mr. Clark's class was excited today. Pets were 3 ... 11

Mr. Clark's class was excited today. Pets were — 11

allowed in school today! The children had brought — 19

puppies, cats, and a rabbit. There were also a lizard, — 29

a snake, two hamsters, a turtle, and even a chicken. — 39

Each boy and girl wrote a story about his or her pet and — 52

read it aloud. — 55

Soon it was lunchtime. The children left the animals — 64

in the classroom. As soon as the door was closed, the — 75

animals started to create turmoil. The puppies chased — 83

the cats down an aisle. The hamsters and turtle began — 93

eating the children's work. One puppy tried to bury a — 103

pencil. The rabbit knocked over some paint, and the — 112

paint spilled onto the lizard. The snake crawled into — 121

Mr. Clark's desk, and the chicken deliberately laid an — 130

egg on top of it! — 135

When the class got back from lunch, the children — 144

saw what the pets had done. Quickly they began — 153

cleaning up the mess. Just as they finished, Mr. Clark — 163

walked back in. He pointed at the quiet animals and — 173

said, "I am really enjoying today. We can all take a — 184

lesson from your pets and be so well behaved." — 193

_____ / WCPM

The Busy Night

My friends and I have a band called The Singing Cubs, and we're going to perform in the school talent show. I'm Bobby, the group's lead guitar player and singer. Kim also plays the guitar, and Ralph is our drummer.

The day before the show, the principal made an announcement. All assignments had to be turned in first thing in the morning for those students performing in the show. We knew it would be a busy night.

First Ralph's parents demanded that he clean up his messy room or skip the show. Then to make matters worse, my mother got sick, and I had to help with dinner. I cooked, served, and cleaned up. Eventually dinner was over, and I started my homework.

Just as I finished my book report, Ralph called. I could hear the frustration in his voice. "There's no way I can get my room clean tonight," he complained. Both Kim and I dashed over to Ralph's house. We worked on his room until it was spotless. Nothing would put our performance in jeopardy!

When it came time to perform the next day, we were exhausted. But we were also very proud of ourselves.

The Busy Night

My friends and I have a band called The Singing Cubs, and we're going to perform in the school talent show. I'm Bobby, the group's lead guitar player and singer. Kim also plays the guitar, and Ralph is our drummer.

The day before the show, the principal made an announcement. All assignments had to be turned in first thing in the morning for those students performing in the show. We knew it would be a busy night.

First Ralph's parents demanded that he clean up his messy room or skip the show. Then to make matters worse, my mother got sick, and I had to help with dinner. I cooked, served, and cleaned up. Eventually dinner was over, and I started my homework.

Just as I finished my book report, Ralph called. I could hear the frustration in his voice. "There's no way I can get my room clean tonight," he complained. Both Kim and I dashed over to Ralph's house. We worked on his room until it was spotless. Nothing would put our performance in jeopardy!

When it came time to perform the next day, we were exhausted. But we were also very proud of ourselves.

Line	Word count
	3
	13
	23
	32
	42
	43
	52
	61
	70
	80
	88
	99
	110
	118
	126
	135
	146
	156
	167
	177
	180
	189
	199
	200

_____ / WCPM

Two Ground Birds

Have you ever seen the Road Runner in a cartoon?

A roadrunner is a real bird. Unlike many birds, roadrunners prefer running to flying. There are other desert birds that prefer the ground to the air, too. One of these is the Gambel's quail. Let's take a closer look at these two ground birds.

Roadrunners live throughout the Southwest. These birds are not easily intimidated. They can run at speeds of fifteen miles per hour or more. From their head to their long tail, they can grow to twenty-two inches. Like many birds, they eat spiders and insects. They also eat lizards, snakes, and the eggs of other birds.

Quails also live mainly on the ground. They build their nests and look for food there. The Gambel's quail, like the roadrunner, lives in the Southwest. However, its range does not go as far into Texas as the roadrunner's. This quail grows to about ten inches long. Like other quails, it has a short tail. It also has a pretty reddish head and a black plume that curls toward its face. Quails eat mainly seeds, berries, grasses, and leaves, but some species can eat insects or eggs.

Two Ground Birds

Have you ever seen the Road Runner in a cartoon? | 13

A roadrunner is a real bird. Unlike many birds, | 22
roadrunners prefer running to flying. There are other | 30
desert birds that prefer the ground to the air, too. One | 41
of these is the Gambel's quail. Let's take a closer look at | 53
these two ground birds. | 57

Roadrunners live throughout the Southwest. These | 63
birds are not easily intimidated. They can run at speeds | 73
of fifteen miles per hour or more. From their head to | 84
their long tail, they can grow to twenty-two inches. Like | 94
many birds, they eat spiders and insects. They also eat | 104
lizards, snakes, and the eggs of other birds. | 112

Quails also live mainly on the ground. They build | 121
their nests and look for food there. The Gambel's quail, | 131
like the roadrunner, lives in the Southwest. However, its | 140
range does not go as far into Texas as the roadrunner's. | 151
This quail grows to about ten inches long. Like other | 161
quails, it has a short tail. It also has a pretty reddish | 173
head and a black plume that curls toward its face. | 183
Quails eat mainly seeds, berries, grasses, and leaves, | 191
but some species can eat insects or eggs. | 199

_____ / WCPM

La Brea Tar Pits

"Don't touch that. It's dirty and sticky!" Have your parents ever said that to you? Well maybe someone should say that to a bunch of scientists in Los Angeles, California. Day in, day out, they spend their time digging around in tar.

What are these scientists doing? They are seeking a special kind of bone—the bones of prehistoric animals. The La Brea Tar Pits are located right in the center of Los Angeles. So far over one million bones have been pulled from the pits. They include the bones of mammoths, giant sloths, dire wolves, saber-toothed cats, insects, and birds.

No one knows how these bones got there. Scientists think that animals might have come bounding into the pits. They would have gotten stuck in the tar and been unable to climb out. Eventually they died, and their bones settled in the tar.

The scientists have the responsibility of taking care of the bones. They carefully clean them and sort them into groups. These clever scientists also have ways to date the bones they find. The oldest ones date back 46,800 years! From these bones, we are learning important things about the last Ice Age.

La Brea Tar Pits 4

"Don't touch that. It's dirty and sticky!" Have your 13

parents ever said that to you? Well maybe someone 22

should say that to a bunch of scientists in Los Angeles, 33

California. Day in, day out, they spend their time 42

digging around in tar. 46

What are these scientists doing? They are seeking 54

a special kind of bone—the bones of prehistoric 63

animals. The La Brea Tar Pits are located right in the 74

center of Los Angeles. So far over one million bones 84

have been pulled from the pits. They include the bones 94

of mammoths, giant sloths, dire wolves, saber-toothed 101

cats, insects, and birds. 105

No one knows how these bones got there. 113

Scientists think that animals might have come bounding 121

into the pits. They would have gotten stuck in the tar 132

and been unable to climb out. Eventually they died, and 142

their bones settled in the tar. 148

The scientists have the responsibility of taking 155

care of the bones. They carefully clean them and sort 165

them into groups. These clever scientists also have 173

ways to date the bones they find. The oldest ones date 184

back 46,800 years! From these bones, we are learning 193

important things about the last Ice Age. 200

_____ / WCPM

Amy and Tom

Amy and Tom are twins. Although Amy was born first, her parents insist that does not give her an advantage and that she and her brother must take turns. Sometimes this is easy, and other times it is difficult.

Dad asks the children whether they want to go to the library. Amy and Tom race to the minivan. They each attempt to get in the front seat. Dad asks whose turn it is to ride up front. Amy and Tom both shout, "Mine!" When Dad announces it is Amy's turn, Amy squeezes past Tom and jumps into the front seat. They immediately start quarreling. "Quiet!" commands Dad. "If you are going to squabble, I will turn this vehicle around and return home."

After they return from the library, Tom and Amy turn the TV on and start arguing about whose turn it is to pick the show. Dad asks whose turn it is. Tom and Amy both declare, "Mine!" When Dad tells Tom to select the show, Amy complains it is an injustice.

After dinner, Mom asks whose turn it is to wash the dishes. When Amy says, "His!" and Tom says, "Hers!" Mom and Dad laugh.

Amy and Tom

        3

Amy and Tom are twins. Although Amy was born   12
first, her parents insist that does not give her an   22
advantage and that she and her brother must take   31
turns. Sometimes this is easy, and other times it is   41
difficult.   42

Dad asks the children whether they want to go   51
to the library. Amy and Tom race to the minivan. They   62
each attempt to get in the front seat. Dad asks whose   73
turn it is to ride up front. Amy and Tom both shout,   85
"Mine!" When Dad announces it is Amy's turn, Amy   94
squeezes past Tom and jumps into the front seat. They   104
immediately start quarreling. "Quiet!" commands Dad.   110
"If you are going to squabble, I will turn this vehicle   121
around and return home."   125

After they return from the library, Tom and Amy   134
turn the TV on and start arguing about whose turn   144
it is to pick the show. Dad asks whose turn it is. Tom   157
and Amy both declare, "Mine!" When Dad tells Tom to   167
select the show, Amy complains it is an injustice.   176

After dinner, Mom asks whose turn it is to wash the   187
dishes. When Amy says, "His!" and Tom says, "Hers!"   196
Mom and Dad laugh.   200

_____ / WCPM

Trip to the North Pole

In the Far North, a group of men struggled against frigid wind. It was sixty degrees below zero! The explorers wore thick fur parkas, gloves, and boots. Some thought they were fools and should go back. But Robert Peary and Matthew Henson wanted to be the first to reach the North Pole, so they pressed on.

Before 1909, no one had ever been to the North Pole. In the Far North, it is light for six months and dark for six months. The team could not cross the ice in the dark. But it would not help to wait too long to leave. The summer Sun could melt the ice on the team's way back. The ice in the Arctic often has cracks. They are caused by Earth's movement and the pull of the Moon's gravity. The ice cracks could split open at any time, plunging the men into the freezing water.

Peary and Henson had tried to reach the North Pole twice before. Both times they had been beaten by the freezing winds, huge blocks of ice, and starvation. Could they make it this time? From their viewpoint, they would not have another chance.

Trip to the North Pole

	5

In the Far North, a group of men struggled 14
against frigid wind. It was sixty degrees below zero! 23
The explorers wore thick fur parkas, gloves, and boots. 32
Some thought they were fools and should go back. But 42
Robert Peary and Matthew Henson wanted to be the 51
first to reach the North Pole, so they pressed on. 61

Before 1909, no one had ever been to the North 71
Pole. In the Far North, it is light for six months and dark 84
for six months. The team could not cross the ice in the 96
dark. But it would not help to wait too long to leave. 108
The summer Sun could melt the ice on the team's way 119
back. The ice in the Arctic often has cracks. They are 130
caused by Earth's movement and the pull of the Moon's 140
gravity. The ice cracks could split open at any time, 150
plunging the men into the freezing water. 157

Peary and Henson had tried to reach the North Pole 167
twice before. Both times they had been beaten by the 177
freezing winds, huge blocks of ice, and starvation. Could 186
they make it this time? From their viewpoint, they would 196
not have another chance. 200

_____ / WCPM

Pizza Party

The fans cheered wildly when Central's basketball team won their fifth game in a row. The team had struggled all year, but now the team led its division. Teammates Shawn and Billy wanted to celebrate, so Shawn's father suggested everyone meet at their house for pizza.

"That's an awesome idea, Mr. Potter!" Billy replied. While Shawn's father went to get his minivan, the other team members asked their parents for permission to attend the pizza party. Billy, Krista, and Jordan got a ride with Mr. Potter. Everyone else rode with their parents or grandparents. On the way home, Mr. Potter picked up two large pizzas.

Nick and Ray arrived at Shawn's house first. They came with their grandfather, who was carrying two large cheese pizzas. Alex, Jamal, and Emma came next. Each carried a large, flat box in his or her hands. The strong aroma was unmistakable—sausage pizza.

"What's happening here?" Shawn's father asked, amazed at all the pizza boxes.

Shawn and his friends laughed. "We're hungry, but not that hungry!" they said.

Pizza Party   2

The fans cheered wildly when Central's basketball   9
team won their fifth game in a row. The team had   20
struggled all year, but now the team led its division.   30
Teammates Shawn and Billy wanted to celebrate, so   38
Shawn's father suggested everyone meet at their house   46
for pizza.   48

"That's an awesome idea, Mr. Potter!" Billy replied.   56
While Shawn's father went to get his minivan, the other   66
team members asked their parents for permission to   74
attend the pizza party. Billy, Krista, and Jordan got   83
a ride with Mr. Potter. Everyone else rode with their   93
parents or grandparents. On the way home, Mr. Potter   102
picked up two large pizzas.   107

Nick and Ray arrived at Shawn's house first. They   116
came with their grandfather, who was carrying two   124
large cheese pizzas. Alex, Jamal, and Emma came   132
next. Each carried a large, flat box in his or her hands. The   145
strong aroma was unmistakable—sausage pizza.   151

"What's happening here?" Shawn's father asked,   157
amazed at all the pizza boxes.   163

Shawn and his friends laughed. "We're hungry, but   171
not that hungry!" they said.   176

_____ / WCPM

Pigeons

Another name for a pigeon is a rock dove. Pigeons belong to the same bird family as doves. Doves are clean and very pretty. Pigeons are not.

In cities, pigeons often gather in parks and other places where people eat lunch. These pigeons are looking for food. Sometimes people pull pieces of bread off loaves and feed them to the pigeons. This makes the pigeons greedy, and they pester people for more food.

One type of pigeon is a homing pigeon. These pigeons are helpful. People teach them to fly home from many miles away. These remarkable birds can carry messages or other possessions.

Another type is a passenger pigeon. Passenger pigeons, like wolves, once were numerous in North America. As people moved west, they hunted these helpless creatures, and they rapidly started to die out. By 1880 both were mostly gone from the wilderness.

The last passenger pigeon died in a zoo in 1914. If people could have predicted that there would be no more passenger pigeons, maybe they would not have hunted them.

Pigeons

	1

Another name for a pigeon is a rock dove. Pigeons 11
belong to the same bird family as doves. Doves are 21
clean and very pretty. Pigeons are not. 28

In cities, pigeons often gather in parks and other 37
places where people eat lunch. These pigeons are 45
looking for food. Sometimes people pull pieces of bread 54
off loaves and feed them to the pigeons. This makes the 65
pigeons greedy, and they pester people for more food. 74

One type of pigeon is a homing pigeon. These 83
pigeons are helpful. People teach them to fly home from 93
many miles away. These remarkable birds can carry 101
messages or other possessions. 105

Another type is a passenger pigeon. Passenger 112
pigeons, like wolves, once were numerous in North 120
America. As people moved west, they hunted these 128
helpless creatures, and they rapidly started to die out. 137
By 1880 both were mostly gone from the wilderness. 146

The last passenger pigeon died in a zoo in 1914. 156
If people could have predicted that there would be no 166
more passenger pigeons, maybe they would not have 174
hunted them. 176

_____ / WCPM

Benedict Arnold

Should we remember Benedict Arnold as a good guy or a bad guy? The answer is unclear. If Arnold could undo his actions, would he?

Arnold started his career as an American fighter. At that time, his primary aim was to end British rule. In 1775 he helped to capture an important fort from the British. Later that year, he led over a thousand soldiers into Canada. Wounded in battle, he earned a promotion. For the next five years, the brave fighter served in battle after battle. In 1777 he led a daring attack against the center of the British line at Saratoga.

Yet in 1780, this same fighter did an unlikely thing. He plotted to hand West Point over to the British in exchange for money. What was his motive? People who look back at history are unsure. Some say he grew resentful when he was passed over for a promotion. Others say he was deeply in debt and had few friends.

After his plot failed, Arnold escaped and joined the British army. He fought openly against his country. Hated in America and not trusted in England, he died a lonely, poor, and unhappy man in 1801.

Progress-Monitoring
Assessments
SESSIONS 3.29, 3.30

Benedict Arnold

Should we remember Benedict Arnold as a good 10

guy or a bad guy? The answer is unclear. If Arnold 21

could undo his actions, would he? 27

Arnold started his career as an American fighter. 35

At that time, his primary aim was to end British rule. 46

In 1775 he helped to capture an important fort from 56

the British. Later that year, he led over a thousand 66

soldiers into Canada. Wounded in battle, he earned a 75

promotion. For the next five years, the brave fighter 84

served in battle after battle. In 1777 he led a daring 95

attack against the center of the British line at Saratoga. 105

Yet in 1780, this same fighter did an unlikely thing. 115

He plotted to hand West Point over to the British in 126

exchange for money. What was his motive? People 134

who look back at history are unsure. Some say he grew 145

resentful when he was passed over for a promotion. 154

Others say he was deeply in debt and had few friends. 165

After his plot failed, Arnold escaped and joined 173

the British army. He fought openly against his country. 182

Hated in America and not trusted in England, he died 192

a lonely, poor, and unhappy man in 1801. 200

_____ / WCPM

Volcano

We can walk on Earth's outside layer, called the crust, without burning our feet. But the temperature inside the earth is incredibly hot. It's hot enough to melt rock!

As rock below the surface melts, it forms underground pools. Eventually, solid rock squeezes the pools from all sides. Heat and pressure start to build.

The melted rock pushes in an upward motion and shoots through a fracture in Earth's crust. As the rock cools on the surface, it forms a mound. The mound builds as more melted rock pushes out. Over time a huge mountain, called a volcano, is formed.

A volcano might look like any other mountain, but it is very different. The pool of melted rock remains below the surface. In time heat and pressure can build up again. Before long the hot melted rock and gases explode out of the mountain. The volcano is erupting. Try to get a mental picture of flaming liquid rock shooting out of a mountain. It is truly an amazing sight! But if you want to personally view an eruption, you should do so from a distance. Volcanic eruptions can be extremely dangerous, destroying everything in their path.

Volcano

We can walk on Earth's outside layer, called the 10

crust, without burning our feet. But the temperature 18

inside the earth is incredibly hot. It's hot enough to 28

melt rock! 30

As rock below the surface melts, it forms 38

underground pools. Eventually, solid rock squeezes the 45

pools from all sides. Heat and pressure start to build. 55

The melted rock pushes in an upward motion and 64

shoots through a fracture in Earth's crust. As the rock 74

cools on the surface, it forms a mound. The mound 84

builds as more melted rock pushes out. Over time a 94

huge mountain, called a volcano, is formed. 101

A volcano might look like any other mountain, but 110

it is very different. The pool of melted rock remains 120

below the surface. In time heat and pressure can build 130

up again. Before long the hot melted rock and gases 140

explode out of the mountain. The volcano is erupting. 149

Try to get a mental picture of flaming liquid rock 159

shooting out of a mountain. It is truly an amazing sight! 170

But if you want to personally view an eruption, you 180

should do so from a distance. Volcanic eruptions can 189

be extremely dangerous, destroying everything in 195

their path. 197

_____ / WCPM

The Mouse House

Mrs. Hill told the students to "build a better mouse house." It needed to be simple but practical. After I thought about the design for a few minutes, I decided to use an empty carton my mother had thrown out. First I cut little air holes in the top for my mouse, Jim. They were big enough to let in plenty of air but not so big that he could escape through one. Next I cut out a door for the house and added water and food dishes and some comfortable rags for his bed.

I placed my pet mouse into his new house and brought my mouse house to school. The class was quiet as Mrs. Hill walked around the room. She carefully examined all of the houses. When she came to mine, she opened the door. Out leaped Jim! He landed on the floor and scampered under her desk. I suddenly realized that I was the only one who had brought a real mouse!

All the students tried to catch Jim, but Mrs. Hill was the one who caught him. She said that both Jim and my mouse house were terrific.

The Mouse House

Mrs. Hill told the students to "build a better mouse	13

    Mrs. Hill told the students to "build a better mouse   13
house." It needed to be simple but practical. After I   23
thought about the design for a few minutes, I decided   33
to use an empty carton my mother had thrown out.   43
First I cut little air holes in the top for my mouse, Jim.   56
They were big enough to let in plenty of air but not so   69
big that he could escape through one. Next I cut out a   81
door for the house and added water and food dishes   91
and some comfortable rags for his bed.   98

    I placed my pet mouse into his new house and   108
brought my mouse house to school. The class was quiet   118
as Mrs. Hill walked around the room. She carefully   127
examined all of the houses. When she came to mine,   137
she opened the door. Out leaped Jim! He landed on   147
the floor and scampered under her desk. I suddenly   156
realized that I was the only one who had brought a   167
real mouse!   169

    All the students tried to catch Jim, but Mrs. Hill was   180
the one who caught him. She said that both Jim and   191
my mouse house were terrific.   196

_____ / WCPM

Wilma Rudolph

Wilma Rudolph is a distinguished track star. She was the first American woman to win three gold medals in a single Olympics. She also received many honors of great significance. One honor was the Sullivan Award as the country's top amateur athlete.

At the age of four, Wilma was stricken with polio. She survived, but doctors said she would never walk again. Yet Wilma would not give up, and she worked intently to beat the odds. By the time she was eight, she could walk with a leg brace. At the age of eleven, she put aside her leg brace for good. She went on to play basketball and run on the track team in high school and college.

At the 1960 Olympic Games, Wilma was the star of the American team. She won gold medals and set world records in three events—the 100-meter dash, the 200-meter dash, and the 400-meter relay.

Wilma later became a coach and a teacher. She also wrote a book about her life. In it she told of the obstacles she had to overcome in her life. This very remarkable woman should be an inspiration to all Americans and to athletes everywhere.

Wilma Rudolph

	2

Wilma Rudolph is a distinguished track star. She   10

was the first American woman to win three gold medals   20

in a single Olympics. She also received many honors of   30

great significance. One honor was the Sullivan Award   38

as the country's top amateur athlete.   44

     At the age of four, Wilma was stricken with polio.   54

She survived, but doctors said she would never walk   63

again. Yet Wilma would not give up, and she worked   73

intently to beat the odds. By the time she was eight, she   85

could walk with a leg brace. At the age of eleven, she   97

put aside her leg brace for good. She went on to play   109

basketball and run on the track team in high school   119

and college.   121

     At the 1960 Olympic Games, Wilma was the star   130

of the American team. She won gold medals and set   140

world records in three events—the 100-meter dash, the   149

200-meter dash, and the 400-meter relay.   155

     Wilma later became a coach and a teacher. She   164

also wrote a book about her life. In it she told of the   177

obstacles she had to overcome in her life. This very   187

remarkable woman should be an inspiration to all   195

Americans and to athletes everywhere.   200

_____ / WCPM

Grades 4–6

Progress-Monitoring Assessments

Forms 1–21

Crayons

Crayons are fun to use, but do you know how they are made? The first step in making crayons is to make the color. A lot of water is mixed with other materials to make each color. Then most of the water is squeezed out. This leaves a dense cake of color that has only a little water left in it.

Next people break up these cakes of color. They put them into ovens to dry out the water and bake the cakes for many hours at a very high heat. The cakes come out of the oven as hard lumps of color. They are dry and have no more water in them.

These hard lumps of color are put in a machine that breaks them into a powder. Then people pour the powder into bags and send them to the place where the crayons are made.

At the crayon factory, the colored powder is mixed into big tanks of hot wax. There are different tanks of wax for each color. The colored wax is then poured into crayon molds. Cold water is poured over the hot wax. It cools the wax and makes it hard. After the wax is hard, it comes out of the molds. Paper is wrapped around each piece, and the crayons are put into boxes.

Crayons

	1

Crayons are fun to use, but do you know how they | 12

are made? The first step in making crayons is to make | 23

the color. A lot of water is mixed with other materials | 34

to make each color. Then most of the water is squeezed | 45

out. This leaves a dense cake of color that has only a | 57

little water left in it. | 62

Next people break up these cakes of color. They put | 72

them into ovens to dry out the water and bake the cakes | 84

for many hours at a very high heat. The cakes come out | 96

of the oven as hard lumps of color. They are dry and | 108

have no more water in them. | 114

These hard lumps of color are put in a machine | 124

that breaks them into a powder. Then people pour the | 134

powder into bags and send them to the place where the | 145

crayons are made. | 148

At the crayon factory, the colored powder is mixed | 157

into big tanks of hot wax. There are different tanks of | 168

wax for each color. The colored wax is then poured into | 179

crayon molds. Cold water is poured over the hot wax. It | 190

cools the wax and makes it hard. After the wax is hard, | 202

it comes out of the molds. Paper is wrapped around each | 213

piece, and the crayons are put into boxes. | 221

_____ / WCPM

Monarch Butterflies

What has orange wings with black veins and flies? It's a monarch butterfly. As soon as the monarch is transformed from a caterpillar into a butterfly, it's on the move. The monarch can't walk on its spindly legs, but it's an extremely effective flier.

Northern butterflies typically do not migrate between north and south, but monarchs are the exception. They migrate just like some birds. That is, they move from one region to another as the seasons change. In the autumn, monarchs fly south to Mexico. They do not travel alone. Instead they fly in huge flocks of hundreds or even thousands of monarch butterflies. When they rest at night, they sometimes cover an entire tree!

When they reach their destination in Mexico, the monarchs spend the winter eating. As spring approaches, the monarchs head back north. However, this time they fly alone. During the trip, the female monarchs lay their eggs. The butterflies will die before they finish their journey. Their eggs later hatch, and a new generation of monarchs begins. Their offspring return to the northern starting point, where they lay their eggs on milkweed plants.

So the next time you see one of these winged wonders, consider the incredible journey this little butterfly will make. It is a truly remarkable creature!

Monarch Butterflies

What has orange wings with black veins and flies? 11
It's a monarch butterfly. As soon as the monarch is 21
transformed from a caterpillar into a butterfly, it's on the 31
move. The monarch can't walk on its spindly legs, but it's 42
an extremely effective flier. 46

Northern butterflies typically do not migrate between 53
north and south, but monarchs are the exception. They 62
migrate just like some birds. That is, they move from one 73
region to another as the seasons change. In the autumn, 83
monarchs fly south to Mexico. They do not travel alone. 93
Instead they fly in huge flocks of hundreds or even 103
thousands of monarch butterflies. When they rest at 111
night, they sometimes cover an entire tree! 118

When they reach their destination in Mexico, the 126
monarchs spend the winter eating. As spring approaches, 134
the monarchs head back north. However, this time they 143
fly alone. During the trip, the female monarchs lay their 153
eggs. The butterflies will die before they finish their 162
journey. Their eggs later hatch, and a new generation 171
of monarchs begins. Their offspring return to the 179
northern starting point, where they lay their eggs on 188
milkweed plants. 190

So the next time you see one of these winged 200
wonders, consider the incredible journey this little 207
butterfly will make. It is a truly remarkable creature! 216

_____ / WCPM

The Library Books

Maria cautiously entered the library and stooped low as she attempted to hide from the librarian's sight. Her library books were overdue for the fourth time.

"How careless, Maria!" scolded Mrs. Columbo, the librarian. "You have to be more responsible. Somebody might be waiting for one of these books."

"I know," Maria shamefully replied. "I forgot all about the books. By the time I remembered, there was no way to get here soon enough. I need to create a reliable invention that can transfer the books back to the library more quickly."

Maria had one zany idea after another. "I could blast the books to the library through a flexible hose," she suggested.

"That might be harmful to the books," Mrs. Columbo observed.

Unwilling to admit defeat, Maria silently pondered and then exclaimed, "I could build a miniature plane out of bicycle parts and fly the books to the library!"

"That would be a most bizarre contraption, and I'm not sure whether it would work," Mrs. Columbo remarked. "Do you even have the skills that are required to construct a plane?"

Maria reluctantly admitted that she did not. Suddenly, a brilliant idea popped into her head. "If I write a message and tape it to my backpack, it will surely remind me to bring the books back when they're due."

Mrs. Columbo smiled in approval and gave Maria her first compliment. "I'm impressed with your sensible idea. You can put it into practice with the books you check out today."

The Library Books   3

Maria cautiously entered the library and stooped low as   12

she attempted to hide from the librarian's sight. Her library   22

books were overdue for the fourth time.   29

"How careless, Maria!" scolded Mrs. Columbo, the   36

librarian. "You have to be more responsible. Somebody might   45

be waiting for one of these books."   52

"I know," Maria shamefully replied. "I forgot all about the   62

books. By the time I remembered, there was no way to get   74

here soon enough. I need to create a reliable invention that   85

can transfer the books back to the library more quickly."   95

Maria had one zany idea after another. "I could blast the   106

books to the library through a flexible hose," she suggested.   116

"That might be harmful to the books," Mrs. Columbo   125

observed.   126

Unwilling to admit defeat, Maria silently pondered and   134

then exclaimed, "I could build a miniature plane out of bicycle 145

parts and fly the books to the library!"   153

"That would be a most bizarre contraption, and I'm not   163

sure whether it would work," Mrs. Columbo remarked.   171

"Do you even have the skills that are required to construct   182

a plane?"   184

Maria reluctantly admitted that she did not. Suddenly, a   193

brilliant idea popped into her head. "If I write a message and   205

tape it to my backpack, it will surely remind me to bring the   218

books back when they're due."   223

Mrs. Columbo smiled in approval and gave Maria her first   233

compliment. "I'm impressed with your sensible idea. You can   242

put it into practice with the books you check out today."   253

_____ / WCPM

Louis Braille

Louis Braille was born in France in 1809. At the age of three, he had an accident in his father's workshop and became completely blind. When Louis was ten, he attended the Royal Institute for Blind Youth in Paris.

An intelligent boy, Louis learned to read. This was not an easy accomplishment. Initially, books for the blind were rare and physically difficult to use. The school had only three books in its library. Each book was divided into twenty parts, and each part weighed more than twenty pounds. A person read the text by touching the huge raised letters on each page. Shortly after Louis arrived at the school, a soldier came to visit. He had invented a system called "night writing." It had been created to be used by the army as a secret code at night. It consisted of raised dots and dashes on thin cardboard. The problem was that it was too complicated. As a result, Louis decided to improve it.

Louis worked day and night. He used only the dots and found that a "cell" made with up to six dots could be changed to form sixty-three different patterns. Using his six-dot cell, he made a separate pattern for each letter of the alphabet. He also made patterns for numbers, for punctuation marks, and even for musical notes. Today this incredible system is used by a multitude of people all over the world.

Louis Braille

	2

Louis Braille was born in France in 1809. At the age **13**

of three, he had an accident in his father's workshop **23**

and became completely blind. When Louis was ten, he **32**

attended the Royal Institute for Blind Youth in Paris. **41**

An intelligent boy, Louis learned to read. This was **50**

not an easy accomplishment. Initially, books for the **58**

blind were rare and physically difficult to use. The school **68**

had only three books in its library. Each book was **78**

divided into twenty parts, and each part weighed more **87**

than twenty pounds. A person read the text by touching **97**

the huge raised letters on each page. Shortly after Louis **107**

arrived at the school, a soldier came to visit. He had **118**

invented a system called "night writing." It had been **127**

created to be used by the army as a secret code at night. **140**

It consisted of raised dots and dashes on thin cardboard. **150**

The problem was that it was too complicated. As a **160**

result, Louis decided to improve it. **166**

Louis worked day and night. He used only the **175**

dots and found that a "cell" made with up to six dots **187**

could be changed to form sixty-three different patterns. **195**

Using his six-dot cell, he made a separate pattern for **205**

each letter of the alphabet. He also made patterns **214**

for numbers, for punctuation marks, and even for **222**

musical notes. Today this incredible system is used by a **232**

multitude of people all over the world. **239**

_____ / WCPM

Margaret Todd, Nurse

I am Margaret Todd, a nurse in a field hospital here in Virginia. When my brother became a soldier in the Union army, I, too, wanted to assist the cause. Being accustomed to hard work, I decided to become a nurse. I came to this area three months ago when my brother's company was sent here. Today, our soldiers have been involved in a fierce battle, with many wounded soldiers arriving at the hospital, where the other nurses and I have been treating them. It is demanding, heartbreaking work.

Suddenly, I hear my brother's voice calling "Margaret," and I grab my medical bag and sprint out onto the field. I am taken aback at the sight of my brother slumped against a cannon, barely awake, and holding his shoulder.

"What happened?" I ask.

"The cannon recoiled and twisted my shoulder out of its socket," he confesses. I urge James to come to the hospital, but he shakes his head with determination. "I can't leave until the enemy departs," he states emphatically. "It is urgent that someone fire the cannon."

I look around and see that nobody is nearby. I hear the sounds of fighting beginning anew and realize everyone is engaged in combat.

I say, "James, you cannot fire the cannon with a dislocated shoulder. You go. I have watched cannons being fired."

I feel afraid, but I set my fear aside and prepare the cannon. I will be brave and defend the soldiers.

Margaret Todd, Nurse   3

I am Margaret Todd, a nurse in a field hospital here in   15

Virginia. When my brother became a soldier in the Union   25

army, I, too, wanted to assist the cause. Being accustomed   35

to hard work, I decided to become a nurse. I came to this   48

area three months ago when my brother's company was   57

sent here. Today, our soldiers have been involved in a   67

fierce battle, with many wounded soldiers arriving at the   76

hospital, where the other nurses and I have been treating   86

them. It is demanding, heartbreaking work.   92

Suddenly, I hear my brother's voice calling "Margaret,"   100

and I grab my medical bag and sprint out onto the field.   112

I am taken aback at the sight of my brother slumped   123

against a cannon, barely awake, and holding his shoulder.   132

"What happened?" I ask.   136

"The cannon recoiled and twisted my shoulder out   144

of its socket," he confesses. I urge James to come to the   156

hospital, but he shakes his head with determination.   164

"I can't leave until the enemy departs," he states   173

emphatically. "It is urgent that someone fire the cannon."   182

I look around and see that nobody is nearby. I   192

hear the sounds of fighting beginning anew and realize   201

everyone is engaged in combat.   206

I say, "James, you cannot fire the cannon with a   216

dislocated shoulder. You go. I have watched cannons   224

being fired."   226

I feel afraid, but I set my fear aside and prepare the   238

cannon. I will be brave and defend the soldiers.   247

_____ / WCPM

Katie's Surprise

Katie stepped out of the plane into a burst of scorching desert heat. Although it was October, it felt like she was walking into an oven. Across the runway, her father eagerly waited in the terminal for them to arrive. "I hate this place and don't want to move here," she thought with a frown. "Why, oh why, did Dad take this new job and move us to this horrible place? After two months of this stifling heat, I'll be missing New York's December slush!"

Her mother nudged Katie, interrupting her thoughts. "Dad's waving, Katie," her mom prompted. Katie automatically waved back, trying hard to hide her unhappiness and discouragement.

Dad undoubtedly looked tan and cheerful. Perhaps in a few weeks she'd look that happy, too, and have forgotten this miserable, lonely feeling. She willed herself not to cry. "Stop it," she reasoned with herself. "You're not a kid anymore—you're practically a teenager!"

After a short drive, Katie exited the car to find herself in front of a one-story house surrounded by cactus plants. "Come around back," Dad said with way too much enthusiasm. "I want to show you something."

"More cactus plants, I bet," thought Katie as she halfheartedly trudged along behind him and thought wistfully about her friends back home.

When Katie stepped around to the back, she couldn't believe her eyes! A great amber-colored horse gazed at her with curiosity from a corral. "Dad!" she exclaimed in astonished delight, her loneliness suddenly melting away.

Katie's Surprise

	2
Katie stepped out of the plane into a burst of	12
scorching desert heat. Although it was October, it felt	21
like she was walking into an oven. Across the runway, her	32
father eagerly waited in the terminal for them to arrive. "I	43
hate this place and don't want to move here," she thought	54
with a frown. "Why, oh why, did Dad take this new job and	67
move us to this horrible place? After two months of this	78
stifling heat, I'll be missing New York's December slush!"	87
Her mother nudged Katie, interrupting her thoughts.	94
"Dad's waving, Katie," her mom prompted. Katie	101
automatically waved back, trying hard to hide her	109
unhappiness and discouragement.	112
Dad undoubtedly looked tan and cheerful. Perhaps in	120
a few weeks she'd look that happy, too, and have forgotten	131
this miserable, lonely feeling. She willed herself not to	140
cry. "Stop it," she reasoned with herself. "You're not a kid	151
anymore—you're practically a teenager!"	156
After a short drive, Katie exited the car to find herself	167
in front of a one-story house surrounded by cactus plants.	177
"Come around back," Dad said with way too much	186
enthusiasm. "I want to show you something."	193
"More cactus plants, I bet," thought Katie as she	202
halfheartedly trudged along behind him and thought	209
wistfully about her friends back home.	215
When Katie stepped around to the back, she couldn't	224
believe her eyes! A great amber-colored horse gazed at	233
her with curiosity from a corral. "Dad!" she exclaimed in	243
astonished delight, her loneliness suddenly melting away.	250

_____ / WCPM

Jake Does the Dishes

Jake groaned when his father asked him to do the dishes. Of all his household chores, this was the one he disliked the most. Every time he washed the dishes, some disaster occurred. Undoubtedly, today would be no exception. "The sooner I get this over with, the better," Jake reasoned with himself. With a sigh, he walked to the kitchen and began to run hot water in the sink. He didn't notice that a teaspoon was lying in the sink, just under the running faucet. Immediately, water splashed off the teaspoon and splattered all over the walls. Jake just grimaced, decided to ignore it, and continued to fill the sink with hot water.

Then Jake began to squirt dishwashing liquid into the pan, but the bottle bounced from his wet hands. Dishwashing liquid shot out, leaving a sticky mess around the sink. Another sigh escaped from Jake's throat.

Jake continued on, reaching for a stack of dinner plates sitting on the counter. As he reached, his shirtsleeve caught on the handle of a skillet. The skillet shifted, bumping into some saucepans and lids. The pans and lids crashed to the floor, making a tremendous clatter. Little splatters of food from the pans lay all over the floor. At that moment, Jake's father, hearing the racket, ran to the kitchen door. When he saw the incredibly helpless expression on Jake's face, he broke into laughter.

Name _____ Date _____

Jake Does the Dishes

	4
Jake groaned when his father asked him to do the	14
dishes. Of all his household chores, this was the one	24
he disliked the most. Every time he washed the dishes,	34
some disaster occurred. Undoubtedly, today would be no	42
exception. "The sooner I get this over with, the better,"	52
Jake reasoned with himself. With a sigh, he walked to	62
the kitchen and began to run hot water in the sink. He	74
didn't notice that a teaspoon was lying in the sink, just	85
under the running faucet. Immediately, water splashed	92
off the teaspoon and splattered all over the walls. Jake	102
just grimaced, decided to ignore it, and continued to fill	112
the sink with hot water.	117
Then Jake began to squirt dishwashing liquid	124
into the pan, but the bottle bounced from his wet	134
hands. Dishwashing liquid shot out, leaving a sticky	142
mess around the sink. Another sigh escaped from	150
Jake's throat.	152
Jake continued on, reaching for a stack of dinner	161
plates sitting on the counter. As he reached, his	170
shirtsleeve caught on the handle of a skillet. The skillet	180
shifted, bumping into some saucepans and lids. The	188
pans and lids crashed to the floor, making a tremendous	198
clatter. Little splatters of food from the pans lay all	208
over the floor. At that moment, Jake's father, hearing	217
the racket, ran to the kitchen door. When he saw the	228
incredibly helpless expression on Jake's face, he broke	236
into laughter.	238

_____ / WCPM

The King and the Fisherman

A fisherman went out in the predawn to burrow sand mussels along the gravelly shore of a freshwater lake. While he was digging, he heard an angry voice exclaim, "Leave me alone." Probing deeper into the hole, the fisherman gazed in amazement at the sand mussel he had uncovered. It would be truly miraculous if his mussel could speak. "Did you say something?" he inquired uncertainly.

The mussel didn't answer, but his dog replied, "The mussel says to leave him alone."

As the confused fisherman angrily kicked a stone, the stone yelled in a startlingly loud voice, "Hey, cut that out!" Frightened, the fisherman ran along the path to the village, where he met a farmer carrying an enormous turnip. "What's your hurry?" the farmer asked quizzically.

"My mussel is talking to me, my dog is talking to me, and the rock is talking to me!" screamed the bewildered fisherman. "So what's the fuss?" the turnip remarked. "Besides," the farmer's wheelbarrow added, "you shouldn't kick rocks."

The fisherman ran to tell his wife what had happened, and she convinced him to go see the king. The king listened doubtfully as the fisherman told his extraordinary tale. "This is a wild story. Begone before I throw you in prison for disturbing the peace. Do you want to be deprived of your freedom?" As the fisherman quickly departed, the king shook his head. "What a ridiculous story!"

"Yes," the throne agreed. "Imagine, a talking mussel!"

The King and the Fisherman | 5

A fisherman went out in the predawn to burrow sand | 15

mussels along the gravelly shore of a freshwater lake. While | 25

he was digging, he heard an angry voice exclaim, "Leave me | 36

alone." Probing deeper into the hole, the fisherman gazed in | 46

amazement at the sand mussel he had uncovered. It would | 56

be truly miraculous if his mussel could speak. "Did you say | 67

something?" he inquired uncertainly. | 71

The mussel didn't answer, but his dog replied, "The | 80

mussel says to leave him alone." | 86

As the confused fisherman angrily kicked a stone, | 94

the stone yelled in a startlingly loud voice, "Hey, cut that | 105

out!" Frightened, the fisherman ran along the path to the | 115

village, where he met a farmer carrying an enormous turnip. | 125

"What's your hurry?" the farmer asked quizzically. | 132

"My mussel is talking to me, my dog is talking to me, | 144

and the rock is talking to me!" screamed the bewildered | 154

fisherman. "So what's the fuss?" the turnip remarked. | 162

"Besides," the farmer's wheelbarrow added, "you shouldn't | 169

kick rocks." | 171

The fisherman ran to tell his wife what had happened, | 181

and she convinced him to go see the king. The king listened | 193

doubtfully as the fisherman told his extraordinary tale. | 201

"This is a wild story. Begone before I throw you in prison | 213

for disturbing the peace. Do you want to be deprived of | 224

your freedom?" As the fisherman quickly departed, the king | 233

shook his head. "What a ridiculous story!" | 240

"Yes," the throne agreed. "Imagine, a talking mussel!" | 248

_____ / WCPM

Mattie's Dog

On the wintriest day of the year, Mattie's dog, Vista, looked at her with unhappiness written all over his face. Giving in to his pleading look, Mattie decided to brave the cold and timidly ventured out into the frosty air. As they walked, she noticed fresh tracks in the snow. Carefully looking around, she spotted a small, peculiar dog huddled against a rock by the river. With no tag or collar, it clearly was lost. It stared hopefully at Mattie and shivered in the cold. Then Vista barked, and the dog ran off. "It's much too cold for a dog to stay outside for long," Mattie thought, "but I can't help it if Vista keeps scaring it away."

So Mattie headed for home. She told her mother about the lost dog, and together they returned to the river to find it. Her mother wanted to assist Mattie with catching the dog because she knew how important it was to her.

Mattie was almost ready to give up, but at last she spotted the dog. She called to it encouragingly, but it jumped onto a rock. Mattie felt like she was making progress and knelt down. The little dog leaped into her arms and began licking her face.

Mattie and her mother took the dog home. Weeks later, the little dog's owner still could not be found. So that is how Wrigley, the friendliest dog in the world, came to be a part of Mattie's family.

Mattie's Dog

	2
On the wintriest day of the year, Mattie's dog, Vista,	12
looked at her with unhappiness written all over his face.	22
Giving in to his pleading look, Mattie decided to brave	32
the cold and timidly ventured out into the frosty air.	42
As they walked, she noticed fresh tracks in the snow.	52
Carefully looking around, she spotted a small, peculiar	60
dog huddled against a rock by the river. With no tag or	72
collar, it clearly was lost. It stared hopefully at Mattie	82
and shivered in the cold. Then Vista barked, and the dog	93
ran off. "It's much too cold for a dog to stay outside for	106
long," Mattie thought, "but I can't help it if Vista keeps	117
scaring it away."	120
So Mattie headed for home. She told her mother	129
about the lost dog, and together they returned to the	139
river to find it. Her mother wanted to assist Mattie with	150
catching the dog because she knew how important it	159
was to her.	162
Mattie was almost ready to give up, but at last she	173
spotted the dog. She called to it encouragingly, but it	183
jumped onto a rock. Mattie felt like she was making	193
progress and knelt down. The little dog leaped into her	203
arms and began licking her face.	209
Mattie and her mother took the dog home. Weeks	218
later, the little dog's owner still could not be found. So	229
that is how Wrigley, the friendliest dog in the world,	239
came to be a part of Mattie's family.	247

_____ / WCPM

The Gray Wolf

Long ago, the gray wolf proudly roamed through most of North America. Today, gray wolves are still common in Alaska and parts of Canada. South of Canada, however, few gray wolves are found. What conditions led to this unhappy state of affairs?

People in the United States have long considered wolves to be dangerous. Settlers killed them to protect their families. Ranchers killed them to protect their livestock. For decades, the federal government paid hunters to shoot these unfortunate animals.

In the late 1960s, when the gray wolf population had almost disappeared in this country, public opinion began to change. Many people began to see wolves as a valuable part of the natural environment. They believed that wolves should be brought back to our northern forests. Thankfully, many still embrace this cause and are working to increase the gray wolf populations in North America.

In 1995, the federal government began a program to return the gray wolf to parts of its former range. Wolves were brought from Canada into Yellowstone National Park. Since then, wolves have begun to thrive once again in three northern states. But not everyone is pleased. The ranchers fear that wolves will destroy their livestock, and they have demanded an end to the program.

What will be the gray wolf's destiny? Will the gray wolf finally die out in the end? People who care about the wilderness must make sure that this does not happen. Raise awareness and help save the gray wolf!

The Gray Wolf   3

Long ago, the gray wolf proudly roamed through most   12
of North America. Today, gray wolves are still common in   22
Alaska and parts of Canada. South of Canada, however,   31
few gray wolves are found. What conditions led to this   41
unhappy state of affairs?   45

People in the United States have long considered   53
wolves to be dangerous. Settlers killed them to protect   62
their families. Ranchers killed them to protect their   70
livestock. For decades, the federal government paid   77
hunters to shoot these unfortunate animals.   83

In the late 1960s, when the gray wolf population had   93
almost disappeared in this country, public opinion began   101
to change. Many people began to see wolves as a valuable   112
part of the natural environment. They believed that   120
wolves should be brought back to our northern forests.   129
Thankfully, many still embrace this cause and are working   138
to increase the gray wolf populations in North America.   147

In 1995, the federal government began a program to   156
return the gray wolf to parts of its former range. Wolves   167
were brought from Canada into Yellowstone National   174
Park. Since then, wolves have begun to thrive once again   184
in three northern states. But not everyone is pleased. The   194
ranchers fear that wolves will destroy their livestock, and 203
they have demanded an end to the program.   211

What will be the gray wolf's destiny? Will the gray   221
wolf finally die out in the end? People who care about   232
the wilderness must make sure that this does not happen.   242
Raise awareness and help save the gray wolf!   250

_____ / WCPM

Mr. Downing's Garden

Mr. Downing had only a beginner's knowledge of gardening, so it came as no surprise that his first attempt at a garden since his retirement from his job as a mathematician was a huge disappointment. He had tried everything—plant food, pruning, bug control, and an abundance of water. He even considered building a drainage system or replacing the soil in case there was a toxicity in it. Unfortunately, he was no magician. The garden still looked pitiful.

One day a woman carrying a large package stood by the fence in front of Mr. Downing's house. She called out to him, "Looks like you could use some help." The woman strolled over to the garden, bent down, and immediately began tending the plants.

As Mr. Downing observed her in stunned silence, he heard a soft sound. Looking around, he realized the woman was singing to the plants.

Mr. Downing focused his attention on the woman for quite some time. Finally, she stood up and approached him. "A little music never hurts. Make sure there is no shortage of song, and this garden will retain its beauty."

Mr. Downing looked from her to his garden in amazement. The flowers were blooming, and there were vegetables on the vines! He turned back, thanked the woman, and asked her name.

"Everybody just calls me the plant musician," she responded, with a smile full of song.

Mr. Downing's Garden

Mr. Downing had only a beginner's knowledge	3
	10

Mr. Downing had only a beginner's knowledge — 10
of gardening, so it came as no surprise that his first — 21
attempt at a garden since his retirement from his job as — 32
a mathematician was a huge disappointment. He had — 40
tried everything—plant food, pruning, bug control, and — 48
an abundance of water. He even considered building a — 57
drainage system or replacing the soil in case there was — 67
a toxicity in it. Unfortunately, he was no magician. The — 77
garden still looked pitiful. — 81

One day a woman carrying a large package stood — 90
by the fence in front of Mr. Downing's house. She called — 101
out to him, "Looks like you could use some help." The — 112
woman strolled over to the garden, bent down, and — 121
immediately began tending the plants. — 126

As Mr. Downing observed her in stunned silence, — 134
he heard a soft sound. Looking around, he realized the — 144
woman was singing to the plants. — 150

Mr. Downing focused his attention on the — 157
woman for quite some time. Finally, she stood up and — 167
approached him. "A little music never hurts. Make sure — 176
there is no shortage of song, and this garden will retain — 187
its beauty." — 189

Mr. Downing looked from her to his garden in — 198
amazement. The flowers were blooming, and there were — 206
vegetables on the vines! He turned back, thanked the — 215
woman, and asked her name. — 220

"Everybody just calls me the plant musician," she — 228
responded, with a smile full of song. — 235

_____ / WCPM

The Talent Show

Every year the sixth graders organized a softball game and talent show. With all the excitement this year, Amy and Carla grew convinced they had to enter the show. Because their team was called the Mustangs, the girls decided that dancing in a horse costume would be masterful—Amy would command the front half, Carla the back half.

For an entire weekend, their attention remained focused on constructing the horse's head. Using a collection of ripped paper, they stuck the strips together with paste and then reinforced the shape with a thicker mixture.

Carla's dad volunteered as their assistant. While he sewed the body from fleecy brown fabric, the girls cut their thickest black yarn for the mane and tail. The massive costume looked wonderful. Next Amy's mom taught them a dance to the song "Plains Pony."

Finally show day arrived! As the girls nervously galloped onto the softball diamond, giggles arose from the audience, and someone called, "Hey, you forgot something!" Panicked, Amy peeked out from the horse head—their tail had disappeared!

"Should we leave?" Carla whispered anxiously.

Amy held steadfast. Although the loss of the tail was unfortunate, they could not give up. "Let's pretend we planned it." As the girls danced on regardless, they spotted the tail on home plate. "I'm taking advantage of this misfortune," Amy said, snatching up the tail.

The girls then danced off the field, waving goodbye with the tail. The audience applauded, howling with enjoyment.

The Talent Show 3

Every year the sixth graders organized a softball game 12

and talent show. With all the excitement this year, Amy and 23

Carla grew convinced they had to enter the show. Because 33

their team was called the Mustangs, the girls decided that 43

dancing in a horse costume would be masterful—Amy 52

would command the front half, Carla the back half. 61

For an entire weekend, their attention remained focused 69

on constructing the horse's head. Using a collection of 78

ripped paper, they stuck the strips together with paste and 88

then reinforced the shape with a thicker mixture. 96

Carla's dad volunteered as their assistant. While he 104

sewed the body from fleecy brown fabric, the girls cut their 115

thickest black yarn for the mane and tail. The massive 125

costume looked wonderful. Next Amy's mom taught them a 134

dance to the song "Plains Pony." 140

Finally show day arrived! As the girls nervously 148

galloped onto the softball diamond, giggles arose from the 157

audience, and someone called, "Hey, you forgot something!" 165

Panicked, Amy peeked out from the horse head—their tail 175

had disappeared! 177

"Should we leave?" Carla whispered anxiously. 183

Amy held steadfast. Although the loss of the tail was 193

unfortunate, they could not give up. "Let's pretend we 202

planned it." As the girls danced on regardless, they spotted 212

the tail on home plate. "I'm taking advantage of this 222

misfortune," Amy said, snatching up the tail. 229

The girls then danced off the field, waving goodbye with 239

the tail. The audience applauded, howling with enjoyment. 247

_____ / WCPM

Castles

Huge stone castles were erected in Europe in the Middle Ages. The castle was a home for the lord and lady and their families. In addition, it was a defense against dangerous enemies.

Castles were often built on high mountains. A moat, which was a deep ditch filled with water, surrounded the castle territory. A drawbridge lay across the water and could be raised during an attack. This helped lords and ladies remain victorious in battles.

The great hall was the center of castle life. The lord and lady of the castle shared the living space with most members of the household. Business was performed in the great hall, and it was here that castle members reunited to eat together.

The lord and lady slept at one end of the hall that was curtained off for privacy. Throughout the rest of the hall, servants slept on benches, on straw beds, or on a carpet of rushes on the floor. These rushes, or grasslike plants, were replaced often because they were subjected to grease and food fragments.

Drafts were quite a difficulty inside the castle. Proper chimneys were unknown until the late 1200s. Instead, flues were purposefully cut through the walls to let smoke escape. It was also not until well into the 1200s that carpets and beautiful tapestries appeared. These not only decorated the floors and walls but also fought drafts. Many of these old castles remain standing today.

Castles

	1

Huge stone castles were erected in Europe in the 10
Middle Ages. The castle was a home for the lord and 21
lady and their families. In addition, it was a defense 31
against dangerous enemies. 34

Castles were often built on high mountains. A moat, 43
which was a deep ditch filled with water, surrounded the 53
castle territory. A drawbridge lay across the water and 62
could be raised during an attack. This helped lords and 72
ladies remain victorious in battles. 77

The great hall was the center of castle life. The lord 88
and lady of the castle shared the living space with most 99
members of the household. Business was performed 106
in the great hall, and it was here that castle members 117
reunited to eat together. 121

The lord and lady slept at one end of the hall that 133
was curtained off for privacy. Throughout the rest of the 143
hall, servants slept on benches, on straw beds, or on a 154
carpet of rushes on the floor. These rushes, or grasslike 164
plants, were replaced often because they were subjected 172
to grease and food fragments. 177

Drafts were quite a difficulty inside the castle. 185
Proper chimneys were unknown until the late 1200s. 193
Instead, flues were purposefully cut through the walls 201
to let smoke escape. It was also not until well into the 213
1200s that carpets and beautiful tapestries appeared. 220
These not only decorated the floors and walls but 229
also fought drafts. Many of these old castles remain 238
standing today. 240

_____ / WCPM

Alana's Problem

Alana had never meant to break the china bowl. Rather, she'd always loved its delicate blue markings and patterns. But it was shattered, and now she waited with mounting dread for the phone call destined to come at any instant—the call from Mrs. Lee, their neighbor, informing her mother about the accident.

Having no children of their own, the Lees were especially fond of Alana. When they journeyed out of town together, the Lees paid Alana to cat-sit for Misty. Visiting twice a day, Alana developed a method. She'd refill Misty's food and water bowls, and then afterward she would settle down beside Misty and toss a catnip mouse into the air. It was fun to watch Misty's whiskers twitch. Then the fluffy cat would surprise her with a leap like a rocket, darting after the toy.

How was she to know that Misty would crash into the bowl, knocking it off its stand? In complete horror, Alana had stared at the bowl in fragments on the floor. What could she do but hide the remnants under the sideboard?

Panicked and sad, she had shuffled home to await the phone call. Except three days later, despite the Lees' return, the call did not come. Alana worried about what she should do.

The following morning, Alana awoke, her mind made up. She had to explain. She had to face the consequences. Reaching for her coat, she called to her mother, "Mom, I need to go see Mrs. Lee."

Alana's Problem

	2
Alana had never meant to break the china bowl.	11
Rather, she'd always loved its delicate blue markings	19
and patterns. But it was shattered, and now she waited	29
with mounting dread for the phone call destined to	38
come at any instant—the call from Mrs. Lee, their	48
neighbor, informing her mother about the accident.	55
Having no children of their own, the Lees were	64
especially fond of Alana. When they journeyed out of	73
town together, the Lees paid Alana to cat-sit for Misty.	83
Visiting twice a day, Alana developed a method. She'd	92
refill Misty's food and water bowls, and then afterward	101
she would settle down beside Misty and toss a catnip	111
mouse into the air. It was fun to watch Misty's whiskers	122
twitch. Then the fluffy cat would surprise her with a leap	133
like a rocket, darting after the toy.	140
How was she to know that Misty would crash into	150
the bowl, knocking it off its stand? In complete horror,	160
Alana had stared at the bowl in fragments on the	170
floor. What could she do but hide the remnants under	180
the sideboard?	182
Panicked and sad, she had shuffled home to await	191
the phone call. Except three days later, despite the Lees'	201
return, the call did not come. Alana worried about what	211
she should do.	214
The following morning, Alana awoke, her	220
mind made up. She had to explain. She had to face	231
the consequences. Reaching for her coat, she called	239
to her mother, "Mom, I need to go see Mrs. Lee."	250

_____ / WCPM

My Grandfather's Journey

My grandfather was born in 1898 in a quiet village in southern Italy. In this small society of farmers, people were busy growing food and raising livestock. As a boy, my grandfather cared for the neighborhood horses and toiled in the fields.

By the time my grandfather reached his teens, World War I had broken out in Europe, and, one by one, the surrounding countries joined the conflict. It was only a question of time before Italy, too, would be influenced to enter the war.

The authorities would undoubtedly view my grandfather, an industrious farm boy, as a chief candidate for the Italian army. My great-grandmother realized the threat to her family: she could lose her son to war. Great-grandmother decided to make the ultimate sacrifice. She would send her son to America and risk never seeing him again. At that time, military service for young men was mandatory. My grandfather's family faced a daunting challenge: how to send him across Italy and onto a ship without being discovered.

Early one morning, a horse-drawn cart pulled up to my grandfather's house. When the cart retreated, my grandfather lay unseen beneath the load of hay. Imagine the apprehension the family must have experienced! Thankfully, he arrived safely at a seaport on the east coast of Italy, where he boarded a ship for the first leg of his triumphant journey to America.

My grandfather must have been very courageous!

My Grandfather's Journey   3

My grandfather was born in 1898 in a quiet village   13
in southern Italy. In this small society of farmers, people   23
were busy growing food and raising livestock. As a boy,   33
my grandfather cared for the neighborhood horses and   41
toiled in the fields.   45

By the time my grandfather reached his teens, World   54
War I had broken out in Europe, and, one by one, the   66
surrounding countries joined the conflict. It was only a   75
question of time before Italy, too, would be influenced   84
to enter the war.   88

The authorities would undoubtedly view my   94
grandfather, an industrious farm boy, as a chief   102
candidate for the Italian army. My great-grandmother   109
realized the threat to her family: she could lose her   119
son to war. Great-grandmother decided to make the   127
ultimate sacrifice. She would send her son to America   136
and risk never seeing him again. At that time, military   146
service for young men was mandatory. My grandfather's   154
family faced a daunting challenge: how to send him across   164
Italy and onto a ship without being discovered.   172

Early one morning, a horse-drawn cart pulled up   180
to my grandfather's house. When the cart retreated, my   189
grandfather lay unseen beneath the load of hay. Imagine   198
the apprehension the family must have experienced!   205
Thankfully, he arrived safely at a seaport on the east   215
coast of Italy, where he boarded a ship for the first leg of   228
his triumphant journey to America.   233

My grandfather must have been very courageous!   240

_____ / WCPM

Yard Sales

You have probably seen people having yard sales, especially in summer. They put out banners and organize tables in their yards. Then they estimate prices. They use stickers to label the items that they want to sell. They distribute these items among the tables for people to look at and consider buying.

Yard sales provide a wonderful way to clean clutter out of your house. To have a yard sale, all you need are household articles that are still in suitable condition but that you no longer want. Do not sell things that are rare before you determine how much they are worth!

When pricing, factor in each item's condition. Price each item for less than it would be if it were new. If you do not have enough things to sell, have a friend or neighbor include his or her things in the sale.

Displaying your merchandise in groups makes it easier for customers to find something to buy. For example, put all books in one spot and toys in another location. You can design signs to let people in the neighborhood know about the sale. As the sale progresses, you can lower the prices on items that are not selling.

If your sale goes well, your total at the end of the day will surprise you!

**Progress-Monitoring
Assessments**
SESSIONS 4-6.31, 4-6.32

Yard Sales   2

You have probably seen people having yard sales,   10
especially in summer. They put out banners and   18
organize tables in their yards. Then they estimate prices.   27
They use stickers to label the items that they want to   38
sell. They distribute these items among the tables for   47
people to look at and consider buying.   54

Yard sales provide a wonderful way to clean clutter   63
out of your house. To have a yard sale, all you need are   76
household articles that are still in suitable condition but   85
that you no longer want. Do not sell things that are rare   97
before you determine how much they are worth!   105

When pricing, factor in each item's condition. Price   113
each item for less than it would be if it were new. If   126
you do not have enough things to sell, have a friend or   138
neighbor include his or her things in the sale.   147

Displaying your merchandise in groups makes   153
it easier for customers to find something to buy.   162
For example, put all books in one spot and toys in   173
another location. You can design signs to let people   182
in the neighborhood know about the sale. As the sale   192
progresses, you can lower the prices on items that are   202
not selling.   204

If your sale goes well, your total at the end of the   216
day will surprise you!   220

_____ / WCPM

Earthquakes

An earthquake occurs when huge masses of rock shift and break beneath the surface of the earth. This movement releases energy that travels in all directions in the form of vibrations called seismic waves. Knowing how these waves travel is important to understanding them.

Fast vibrations, known as body waves, move deep inside the earth. Slower waves move along the earth's surface. As body waves pass through the earth, they cause the rock to move in two basic ways. Some body waves, called P waves, push and pull the rock. The S waves slide the rocks from side to side. Because the P waves travel faster, they are first to shake the ground. The S waves that follow further knock and shake the earth.

The long and slow surface waves travel only through the crust, or top layer, of the earth. Although they come after body waves, they tend to produce the most damage and ruin. Surface waves can be either Love waves or ground rolls. The quicker Love waves shift the ground from side to side. The slower ground rolls cause the surface of the earth to roll like waves on the ocean.

It is routinely the ground roll that produces most of the shaking felt from an earthquake. People who feel a ground roll often remember the experience.

Earthquakes

	1
An earthquake occurs when huge masses of rock	9
shift and break beneath the surface of the earth. This	19
movement releases energy that travels in all directions	27
in the form of vibrations called seismic waves.	35
Knowing how these waves travel is important to	43
understanding them.	45

Fast vibrations, known as body waves, move deep 53
inside the earth. Slower waves move along the earth's 62
surface. As body waves pass through the earth, they 71
cause the rock to move in two basic ways. Some body 82
waves, called P waves, push and pull the rock. The S 93
waves slide the rocks from side to side. Because the P 104
waves travel faster, they are first to shake the ground. 114
The S waves that follow further knock and shake 123
the earth. 125

The long and slow surface waves travel only through 134
the crust, or top layer, of the earth. Although they come 145
after body waves, they tend to produce the most damage 155
and ruin. Surface waves can be either Love waves or 165
ground rolls. The quicker Love waves shift the ground 174
from side to side. The slower ground rolls cause the 184
surface of the earth to roll like waves on the ocean. 195

It is routinely the ground roll that produces most of 205
the shaking felt from an earthquake. People who feel a 215
ground roll often remember the experience. 221

_____ / WCPM

Dangerous Hurricanes

A hurricane is a powerful storm with swirling winds. Hurricanes form over water in tropical parts of the North Atlantic and North Pacific Oceans. Most hurricanes in these regions occur between June and November.

A hurricane does not form all at once. First areas of low pressure, called easterly waves, develop in ocean winds. These can grow into a tropical depression with wind speeds of up to thirty-nine miles per hour. The winds can pick up yet more speed, blowing up to seventy-three miles per hour. This is considered a tropical storm. Finally winds over seventy-four miles per hour can form storms that are three hundred miles wide. These storms are known as hurricanes.

The great speed of a hurricane's winds can cause severe damage and harm when it reaches land. This ruthless storm can destroy structures and knock down trees, which are unable to endure the winds. The force of its winds can also create huge waves. The waves, along with heavy rains, may cause flooding. This is yet another danger to life and property.

Because these storms are so perilous, weather forecasters must monitor the Pacific and Atlantic Oceans during hurricane season. If people know that a powerful storm is coming, they can prepare. They can put outdoor things away. They can check doors and windows and tape them shut. They even have the option of leaving their homes before the storm arrives.

Dangerous Hurricanes

A hurricane is a powerful storm with swirling	10
winds. Hurricanes form over water in tropical parts	18
of the North Atlantic and North Pacific Oceans.	26
Most hurricanes in these regions occur between June	34
and November.	36

A hurricane does not form all at once. First areas 46
of low pressure, called easterly waves, develop in 54
ocean winds. These can grow into a tropical depression 63
with wind speeds of up to thirty-nine miles per hour. 73
The winds can pick up yet more speed, blowing up 83
to seventy-three miles per hour. This is considered a 92
tropical storm. Finally winds over seventy-four miles per 100
hour can form storms that are three hundred miles wide. 110
These storms are known as hurricanes. 116

The great speed of a hurricane's winds can cause 125
severe damage and harm when it reaches land. This 134
ruthless storm can destroy structures and knock down 142
trees, which are unable to endure the winds. The force of 153
its winds can also create huge waves. The waves, along 163
with heavy rains, may cause flooding. This is yet another 173
danger to life and property. 178

Because these storms are so perilous, weather 185
forecasters must monitor the Pacific and Atlantic 192
Oceans during hurricane season. If people know that a 201
powerful storm is coming, they can prepare. They can 210
put outdoor things away. They can check doors and 219
windows and tape them shut. They even have the option 229
of leaving their homes before the storm arrives. 237

_____ / WCPM

Pablo's Music

Bugs. Angelica didn't necessarily hate the critters, but ever since her mother purchased her brother Pablo the soundtrack to the movie *Bugs,* he chattered about it constantly. Besides that, he listened to one particular song, "Munching Leaves," endlessly. The song had a catchy tune, the kind that engulfs your brain and leaves you singing it incessantly no matter how hard you strive to stop.

One day Angelica's friend Michelle shot her a curious glance, asking, "Why are you singing about munching leaves?" Just then, Angelica knew she had to do something.

"If I hear that CD once more, I'll begin frothing at the mouth," she complained to her father. Her dad exhaled, admitting that he was caught singing "Don't Bug Me" during an important meeting.

"Can't you tell him not to play it?" Angelica pleaded.

"Would it be fair if I told you not to play your music?" Dad reasoned. Angelica acknowledged his point. Then, mischievously, she smiled with an idea. In the stacks at the local library, Angelica unearthed a CD of folk songs that she had cherished in her childhood. Once home, she began playing it. The inquisitive Pablo peeked in her room. She, however, slammed the door and grinned.

Knocking awkwardly, Pablo stood requesting, "Can I borrow that music?"

"Only if you give it right back," Angelica warned.

Of course, Pablo didn't, which was her goal all along. By the time Angelica started frothing over folk music, the CD was due back at the library.

Pablo's Music

Bugs. Angelica didn't necessarily hate the critters,	2
but ever since her mother purchased her brother Pablo	9
the soundtrack to the movie *Bugs,* he chattered about it	18
constantly. Besides that, he listened to one particular song,	28
"Munching Leaves," endlessly. The song had a catchy tune,	37
the kind that engulfs your brain and leaves you singing it	46
incessantly no matter how hard you strive to stop.	57
	66

One day Angelica's friend Michelle shot her a curious
glance, asking, "Why are you singing about munching
leaves?" Just then, Angelica knew she had to do something.

"If I hear that CD once more, I'll begin frothing at the
mouth," she complained to her father. Her dad exhaled,
admitting that he was caught singing "Don't Bug Me" during
an important meeting.

"Can't you tell him not to play it?" Angelica pleaded.

"Would it be fair if I told you not to play your music?"
Dad reasoned. Angelica acknowledged his point. Then,
mischievously, she smiled with an idea. In the stacks at the
local library, Angelica unearthed a CD of folk songs that
she had cherished in her childhood. Once home, she began
playing it. The inquisitive Pablo peeked in her room. She,
however, slammed the door and grinned.

Knocking awkwardly, Pablo stood requesting, "Can I
borrow that music?"

"Only if you give it right back," Angelica warned.

Of course, Pablo didn't, which was her goal all along. By
the time Angelica started frothing over folk music, the CD
was due back at the library.

Numbers in right margin:
75, 83, 93, 105, 114, 124, 127, 137, 150, 157, 168, 178, 188, 198, 204, 211, 214, 223, 234, 244, 250

_____ / WCPM

Termites

A tall, brown mound rising from the African savannah looks like a tree stump or sculpture, but it isn't. It's a termite mound, home to millions of termites.

To these tiny residents, the mound seems like a comfortable mansion. Sometimes construction of a termite mound can reach as high as twenty feet, looking like a huge sand castle.

The termites build the mound themselves. They mix the absorbent soil with their saliva to make sticky glue, which they use to build the mound walls. The hot African sun bakes the walls until they are hard and resistant.

The inside of the termite mound consists of a maze of tunnels. Tunnels let in air to cool the termites and to help them breathe. The mound also contains rooms, including rooms for food storage. When fresh wood for eating is not available, the termites eat the stored food. Other rooms are nurseries in which young termites hatch and grow.

What happens when the termite eggs hatch in that maze of tunnels and rooms? Each member has its own contribution. Some larvae become dependable workers, who do all the work in the mound. Others become soldiers whose only job is to defend the termite colony.

Still others become new kings and queens, who leave their "home" mound. On delicate wings they fly away on an expedition to found new colonies. Soon other termite mounds rise on the savannah.

Termites

	1

A tall, brown mound rising from the African | 9

savannah looks like a tree stump or sculpture, but it isn't. | 20

It's a termite mound, home to millions of termites. | 29

To these tiny residents, the mound seems like a | 38

comfortable mansion. Sometimes construction of a | 44

termite mound can reach as high as twenty feet, looking | 54

like a huge sand castle. | 59

The termites build the mound themselves. They | 66

mix the absorbent soil with their saliva to make sticky | 76

glue, which they use to build the mound walls. The | 86

hot African sun bakes the walls until they are hard | 96

and resistant. | 98

The inside of the termite mound consists of a maze | 108

of tunnels. Tunnels let in air to cool the termites and | 119

to help them breathe. The mound also contains rooms, | 128

including rooms for food storage. When fresh wood for | 137

eating is not available, the termites eat the stored food. | 147

Other rooms are nurseries in which young termites | 155

hatch and grow. | 158

What happens when the termite eggs hatch in that | 167

maze of tunnels and rooms? Each member has its own | 177

contribution. Some larvae become dependable workers, | 183

who do all the work in the mound. Others become | 193

soldiers whose only job is to defend the termite colony. | 203

Still others become new kings and queens, who leave | 212

their "home" mound. On delicate wings they fly away on | 222

an expedition to found new colonies. Soon other termite | 231

mounds rise on the savannah. | 236

_____ / WCPM

Ferris Wheels

Ferris wheels are fun rides found at carnivals, fairs, and amusement parks. The typical Ferris wheel stands forty to fifty feet high and carries twenty to thirty people. This giant rolling wheel is a spectacular sight. But when was the invention created, and who came up with the idea?

The Ferris wheel was first erected at the World's Columbian Exposition in Chicago in 1893. The design and technology of this prototype came from bridge maker George W. Ferris. He got the idea from looking at the structure of a merry-go-round. The structure had to be adapted so it would function upright.

Ferris's plans called for a vertical wheel that would make every other wheel look small. The wheel was 250 feet in diameter. It had thirty-six cars that carried a total of 2,160 people. Previously no ride had been built on such a grand scale. This enormous wheel was used again in 1904 at the St. Louis Exposition.

You might think that the height of Ferris wheels would cause them to tip over easily, but there have been few accidents involving them. The wheels can withstand winds of sixty miles per hour. Also owners are continually inspecting the rides to make sure they are properly maintained.

No one could predict the Ferris wheel's lasting popularity. Not as thrilling as roller coasters, the multicolored attractions are for those who want a more relaxing ride with a wonderful view.

Ferris Wheels

Ferris wheels are fun rides found at carnivals, fairs,	11
and amusement parks. The typical Ferris wheel stands	19
forty to fifty feet high and carries twenty to thirty	29
people. This giant rolling wheel is a spectacular sight.	38
But when was the invention created, and who came up	48
with the idea?	51
The Ferris wheel was first erected at the World's	60
Columbian Exposition in Chicago in 1893. The design	68
and technology of this prototype came from bridge	76
maker George W. Ferris. He got the idea from looking at	87
the structure of a merry-go-round. The structure had to	96
be adapted so it would function upright.	103
Ferris's plans called for a vertical wheel that would	112
make every other wheel look small. The wheel was 250	122
feet in diameter. It had thirty-six cars that carried a total	133
of 2,160 people. Previously no ride had been built on	143
such a grand scale. This enormous wheel was used again	153
in 1904 at the St. Louis Exposition.	160
You might think that the height of Ferris wheels	169
would cause them to tip over easily, but there have	179
been few accidents involving them. The wheels can	187
withstand winds of sixty miles per hour. Also owners are	197
continually inspecting the rides to make sure they are	206
properly maintained.	208
No one could predict the Ferris wheel's lasting	216
popularity. Not as thrilling as roller coasters, the	224
multicolored attractions are for those who want a more	233
relaxing ride with a wonderful view.	239

_____ / WCPM